Complete Masses

Recent Researches in Music

A-R Editions publishes seven series of critical editions, spanning the history of Western music, American music, and oral traditions.

Recent Researches in the Music of the Middle Ages and Early Renaissance
  Charles M. Atkinson, general editor

Recent Researches in the Music of the Renaissance
  David Crook, general editor

Recent Researches in the Music of the Baroque Era
  Steven Saunders, general editor

Recent Researches in the Music of the Classical Era
  Neal Zaslaw, general editor

Recent Researches in the Music of the Nineteenth and Early Twentieth Centuries
  Rufus Hallmark, general editor

Recent Researches in American Music
  John M. Graziano, general editor

Recent Researches in the Oral Traditions of Music
  Philip V. Bohlman, general editor

Each edition in *Recent Researches* is devoted to works by a single composer or to a single genre. The content is chosen for its high quality and historical importance and is edited according to the scholarly standards that govern the making of all reliable editions.

For information on establishing a standing order to any of our series, or for editorial guidelines on submitting proposals, please contact:

A-R Editions, Inc.
Middleton, Wisconsin

800 736-0070 (North American book orders)
608 836-9000 (phone)
608 831-8200 (fax)
http://www.areditions.com

RECENT RESEARCHES IN THE MUSIC OF THE BAROQUE ERA, 186

Natale Monferrato

Complete Masses

Edited by Jonathan R. J. Drennan

A-R Editions, Inc.
Middleton, Wisconsin

To Lucy, Molly, and Christian

A-R Editions, Inc., Middleton, Wisconsin
© 2014 by A-R Editions, Inc.

All rights reserved. No part of this book may be reproduced or transmitted in any form by any electronic or mechanical means (including photocopying, recording, or information storage and retrieval) without permission in writing from the publisher.

The purchase of this edition does not convey the right to perform it in public, nor to make a recording of it for any purpose. Such permission must be obtained in advance from the publisher.

A-R Editions is pleased to support the use of *Recent Researches* material for study or performance. Please visit our website (www.areditions.com) to apply for permission to perform, record, or otherwise reuse the material in this publication.

Printed in the United States of America

ISBN 978-0-89579-784-1
ISSN 0484-0828

♾ The paper used in this publication meets the minimum requirements of the American National Standard for Information Sciences—Permanence of Paper for Printed Library Materials, ANSI Z39.48-1992.

Contents

Acknowledgments   vii

Introduction   ix
   The Composer   ix
   Mass at San Marco and Monferrato's Mass Settings   xi
   The Dedications   xv
   Notes on Performance   xv
   Notes   xvi

Plates   xix

Missae, ad usum cappellarum, quattuor & quinque vocibus concinendae, Op. 13
   Dedication   2

Messa a cappella prima *(a 4)*
   Kyrie   3
   Gloria   6
   Credo   14
   Sanctus   25
   Agnus Dei   29

Messa a cappella seconda *(a 4)*
   Kyrie   32
   Gloria   35
   Credo   43
   Sanctus   54
   Agnus Dei   58

Messa a cappella terza *(a 4)*
   Kyrie   60
   Gloria   63
   Credo   69
   Sanctus   79
   Agnus Dei   82

Messa a cappella quarta *(a 4)*
   Kyrie   84
   Gloria   87
   Credo   94
   Sanctus   106
   Agnus Dei   110

Messa a cappella quinta *(a 4)*
   Kyrie   113
   Gloria   117
   Credo   123
   Sanctus   132
   Agnus Dei   136

Messa a cappella sesta *(a 5)*
- Kyrie   138
- Gloria   145
- Credo   156
- Sanctus   172
- Agnus Dei   180

Masses from *Messe et Magnificat a quattro voci*, Op. 19
- Dedication   184

Messa a cappella *(a 4)*
- Kyrie   185
- Gloria   189
- Credo   196
- Sanctus   207
- Agnus Dei   211

Messa breve *(a 4)*
- Kyrie   213
- Gloria   215
- Credo   221
- Sanctus   231
- Agnus Dei   233

Critical Report   235
- Sources   235
- Editorial Methods   236
- Critical Notes   237
- Notes   239

Acknowledgments

The research for this edition was funded by the British Academy, London, and was also made possible by the help of many others. First and foremost, I am most grateful to staff at the following institutions for allowing me to consult the surviving source materials for Monferrato's music: the Museo internazionale e biblioteca della musica di Bologna; the Bibliothèque nationale de France, Paris; the Procuratoria di San Marco, Venice; the Biblioteca Nazionale Marciana, Venice; and the Musiksammlung des Grafen von Schönborn-Wiesentheid, Wiesentheid. My thanks extend to the Archivio di Stato, Venice, for granting access to myriad early documents, and to the Hamburger Kunsthalle, Hamburg, for permitting the reproduction of Giovanni Antonio Canal's splendid eighteenth-century depiction of San Marco's interior.

I am also indebted to guides at the church of San Bartolomeo, Venice, who so kindly allowed me to venture into the sacristy to view and photograph both Monferrato's tomb and his bust, especially since this part of the church was undergoing renovation at that time. Also in Venice, Marco Gemmani, the present maestro of San Marco, must be afforded thanks for his prompt answering of my various queries.

There are three special individuals to whom I offer considerable thanks. First, to my good friend Michael Talbot, who extended much expertise with regard to many aspects of this project; I am tremendously grateful to him. Also, to Micky White, who, through possessing a vast knowledge of the Venetian archives, was able to direct my attention to several significant documents. And, last, but not least, to my dear friend J. Donald Cullington for providing expert translations from Latin. Thank you, all!

Introduction

The name of Natale Monferrato (1609/10–85) is likely to be unfamiliar, even to enthusiasts of baroque music. Monferrato was maestro di cappella at the famous church of San Marco, Venice during 1676–85; it was a prestigious position that won him recognition throughout Europe. Monferrato's obscurity today rests firmly on the fact that he was a composer of sacred music, first and foremost, living in an era that has hitherto been of primarily secular interest. His important contribution to music at seventeenth-century San Marco has largely gone unnoticed, having been overshadowed by the works of his far more celebrated predecessors—the secular icons Claudio Monteverdi and Francesco Cavalli—and his better-known successor Giovanni Legrenzi. Ironically, it was the little-known Monferrato who placed music on an even keel at the great Venetian chapel by restoring choral discipline after a long period of decay.

Monferrato's sizable musical output—the vast bulk of which has been neither edited nor studied—is significant in several respects, not least in terms of its mass settings. His extant repertoire of masses is impressive: eight published a cappella works, which form the largest single contribution to the chapel's surviving assortment of early ferial masses. The present publication marks the first attempt to compile and edit the complete corpus of Monferrato's mass music. It is a forgotten repertory that provides not only an invaluable insight into the daily ritual at one of the most important musical institutions in northern Italy during the baroque era, but also an engaging selection of high-quality music suitable for choirs of varied ability.

The Composer

There has been uncertainty regarding the lifespan of Natale Monferrato. The late Denis Arnold speculated that Natale, or Nadal (the Venetian dialectal form of his name),[1] was born around 1615 and died before 12 April 1685. Elsewhere, it is reported that his birth occurred around 1603 and his death before 23 April 1685. However, Monferrato's obituary, which survives in Venice, is specific: according to this document, he died from "fever" and "inflammation" after three days of illness on 13 April 1685 at the impressive age of seventy-five years, which would place his birth during 1609 or 1610.[2]

Monferrato was a priest at the small church of San Bartolomeo (near Venice's well-known Rialto Bridge).[3] More impressive, however, was his post as maestro di cappella of the prestigious ducal church of San Marco—private chapel of Venice's ruling doge. The directorship at San Marco was a highly desirable position, not just within the confines of the Veneto—the islands of Venice and its territories on the Terraferma veneta—but also across Europe. The position offered musical and social prominence, the opportunity to produce musical material for a richly varied liturgical calendar with local elements, financial security, and, importantly, time to pursue interests outside the confines of San Marco.[4] That the post was formerly held by some of Europe's finest musicians—Cipriano de Rore, Gioseffo Zarlino, and Claudio Monteverdi included—is testimony to Monferrato's caliber and reputation.

Going by archival records, Monferrato's involvement in music at San Marco began in the opening months of 1639. On 23 January he was one of four applicants who competed for the post of second organist. Although his application was unsuccessful—the better-known Francesco Cavalli was given the position—Monferrato remained focused on employment at the ducal chapel, for on 22 February he was admitted into the Cappella Marciana—the body of ducal musicians—with an annual salary of sixty ducats (rising to eighty ducats on 12 July 1643).[5]

The death of the maestro Monteverdi during November 1643 was a circumstance that greatly profited Monferrato (then in his early thirties). Giovanni Rovetta (ca. 1596–1668), Monteverdi's able assistant director, was elected maestro in 1644, which in turn left the post of vice-maestro vacant. Curiously, the authorities at San Marco were unhurried about filling the position, for it remained unoccupied until 20 January 1647, when "Pré [Prete] Nadal [Monferrato]" was appointed with the customary introductory annual salary of 120 ducats.[6] Monferrato promptly celebrated his elevation by sending to the Gardano presses an impressive set of *Salmi concertati* for five to eight voices (opus 1, 1647).

The post of vice-maestro was relatively new at San Marco. It was created in 1607 during the tenure of maestro Giovanni Croce (ca. 1557–1609) to help overcome the problem of spatial coordination in the chapel: on those occasions when polychoral music was performed by groups of musicians positioned in different parts of the building, there was a need for a second conductor to relay the beat of the maestro to singers located in the first organ loft. Other tasks were duly expected of the vice-maestro: he was to take charge when his superior was absent and to do those things considered too menial for the maestro (such as training choristers and pupils of the seminary).[7] Monferrato, it seems, was an effective assistant director, for his salary increased to two hundred ducats—the highest level of pay for a vice-maestro—only six years after his appointment; for comparison, it had taken over fourteen years for his predecessor Rovetta to achieve the same sum.[8]

A feasible catalyst for Monferrato's promotion from singer to assistant director was his appointment during 1642 as maestro *di coro* of the Ospedale dei Mendicanti. The Mendicanti, one of four major charitable institutions in Venice, offered a refuge for the sick and disadvantaged (notably orphans), but it was renowned—especially during the eighteenth century—for its accomplished female vocal and instrumental ensembles.[9] Monferrato was paid a handsome salary of 120 ducats for the directorship, but this stipend came with responsibility. Indeed, his renewed contract of employment from 1669 provides a measure of his responsibilities and of the ruling body's eagerness to ensure continued commitment from their maestro (then in his twenty-seventh year of service):

> The priest Nadal is confirmed as choirmaster at a fee of 120 ducats per year and with the following commitments. He is to come to the hospital at least three days a week to instruct the girls. He is to see that the beginners practice their singing, encourage those who show some promise, give periodical reports on the progress made by the girls, before he may receive his half-year's salary. He is to review all the junior girls of the institution and select the competent ones. He is to be alert in his search for girls of ability, even though they may be outside the hospital, and to advise the members in charge of the church and those in charge of welfare, so that these girls may be admitted.[10]

Monferrato's copious collection of twenty-one solo motets, published by Vincenti in 1655 as opus 4, comprises works written solely for students at the Mendicanti. The publication is testimony to the institution's high musical standards, but it also provides useful evidence of the composer's dexterity in the seconda prattica and of developments in musical notation (with, for example, the integration of regular barring). Opus 4 was the first installment in a three-part series of motet publications for solo voices (the second installment is not extant; the third book—opus 6—was published in 1666).

At San Marco, the 1650s marked the beginning of a period of discontent. There was dissatisfaction within the ranks of the Cappella Marciana over the combination of small wages and increased duties, the result being that singers were pursuing, in significant number, secular employments where the money-to-work ratio was considerably more favorable. By 1653, membership had fallen from a standard complement of around forty singers to only twenty-eight.[11] That Monferrato dedicated a publication of virtuosic *Motetti concertati* (Gardano, opus 3) to the procurator Giovanni Correr in 1655 may have been a gesture of loyalty in difficult times. Ironically, despite the fact that the decline stemmed from secularization, the procurators appointed as maestro in 1668 an international star of secular music: Francesco Cavalli.[12] Cavalli was a highly competent maestro, but his eight-year tenure was not without controversy; indeed, through failing to confront the problem of singers' salaries, he lost eighteen further *cantori* to positions in Vienna, Dresden, Warsaw, Brandenburg, Braunschweig, Neuburg, Rome, Naples, Parma, Modena, Loreto, and distant London.[13] It was Monferrato, rather, who took the decisive steps to avoid a potential musical crisis.

Following Cavalli's death, Monferrato was offered the job of maestro di cappella (on 30 April 1676) with the usual obligations, salary (of four hundred ducats), and quarters in the *canonica*. There were two other applicants for the post: one was the chapel's first organist, Pietro Andrea Ziani; the other was the esteemed Giovanni Legrenzi, maestro of the ducal church in Ferrara, who was a close contender in the procurators' ballot for the position. Antonio Sartorio replaced Monferrato as vice-maestro. Monferrato's solution to the falling numbers in the choir was straightforward: he would reduce the membership and, by doing this, pay the remaining singers higher wages. The plan, which was approved on 20 April 1677, involved the reauditioning of singers who had joined the choir during the previous twelve years;[14] predictably, the idea met with some disapproval.[15]

Monferrato's initiative, however, revitalized the choir. The selection process provided space for a wave of highly skilled appointees; in fact, half of the eight singers hired during 1679 alone were paid the chapel's top rate of one hundred ducats. Tuition was provided for choristers through two expert teachers: one was the bass Lodovico Zanchi, admitted in 1676, who taught *canto fermo*; the other, the tenor Ludovico Fuga, was employed in 1682 to provide instruction in counterpoint. That standards improved rapidly as a result of Monferrato's measures is demonstrated by the speed at which singers' salaries increased. For instance, Antonio Pestachi—a later star of the operatic scene—was initially engaged in 1681 at the rate of sixty ducats, but by 1683 he was achieving one hundred ducats. More striking is the example of Bartolomeo Duramano—a later master of ceremonies at San Marco—who entered the choir in 1681 at the salary of thirty ducats but by 1684 was earning one hundred ducats.[16]

Monferrato's resignation from the Mendicanti in 1676 may have been motivated by his promotion at San Marco during that same year. Conversely, he may simply have been eager to find time for new pursuits, one being an interest in music publishing. During his final months as vice-maestro, Monferrato provided the finance and accommodation for a new publishing house in the Rialto district of Venice. The business, which operated from the family home (near the church of San Giovanni Grisostomo), was managed by, and operated under the name of, local printer Giuseppe Sala.[17] All of Monferrato's extant publications from the period 1676–82 were issued via the Sala press. These six collections, all written for use at San Marco, comprise two sets of concerted psalms (opus 11, 1676; opus 16, 1678), two of a cappella masses (opus 13,

1677; opus 19, 1682), one of solo antiphons (opus 17, 1678), and one of concerted motets (opus 18, 1682).[18] The preface to the latter is particularly memorable: in it, Monferrato takes the liberty of thanking the procurators for his promotion to maestro, but he goes on to emphasize that over the past forty years at the ducal chapel, he has presented to them countless collections of sacred compositions. His obvious intimation that his promotion was well deserved evidently found resonance in the procurators' chambers, for he was soon afterward awarded a golden medallion for service.[19]

After nine years as maestro, Monferrato died on 13 April 1685 at the age of seventy-five; the esteemed Giovanni Legrenzi succeeded him ten days later. Requiem masses were celebrated, first at San Marco, and later at San Bartolomeo, where he was laid to rest in the sacristy, and where an impressive bust of him was erected. Monferrato's generosity of character, his musical rank, and his priestly virtues are celebrated on the inscriptions to both his bust and tomb (see plates 1–2). Even though he served under some of the most celebrated figures of the early baroque, Monferrato's last will and testament reveals that he was beholden to the lesser-known Giovanni Rovetta, to the extent that he requested the latter's "grand" polychoral requiem—the setting Rovetta wrote in anticipation of his own death in 1668—for his own funeral.[20]

Monferrato's will is demonstrative of both prosperity and generosity. There were many beneficiaries of his large estate: one was Giovanni Battista Volpe, Giovanni Rovetta's nephew, to whom the deceased bequeathed a muted harpsichord (among other possessions);[21] other beneficiaries included the impoverished souls of the parish of San Bartolomeo—poor women unable to afford marriage, clergymen of limited means, women needing financial help to enter holy orders—who received endowments. The residue went to the Scuola del Sacramento of San Bartolomeo. In return for his charity, Monferrato requested that his death be commemorated annually, and in perpetuity, at the church of San Bartolomeo with the same requiem music performed on the day of his funeral.[22]

Mass at San Marco and Monferrato's Mass Settings

Although Venice was notoriously disobedient to papal rulings, the mass liturgy at its ducal chapel remained strikingly obedient to the Roman Rite. Indeed, San Marco merely adjusted the *Missale Romanum* to facilitate its local customs, a type of procedure that pertained throughout Europe.[23] This modified liturgy, and the long musical traditions associated with it, persisted unchanged until the fall of the Venetian Republic. The abdication of the doge following the invasion of French forces in 1797, and San Marco's consequent change of function (from private ducal chapel to state church), left the mass liturgy essentially unchanged, but there were profound implications for the ceremonial and musical life of the chapel.[24]

San Marco's pre-1797 liturgy is laid out in detail in its surviving ceremonials and missals. Close inspection of these liturgical books reveals that, of the many masses celebrated during the liturgical year, few actually deviated from the Roman Rite, and in the occasional places where modifications occurred, the disparities were unremarkable (as on Holy Thursday).[25] Accordingly, early missals used in that chapel—five of which survive in Venice—are simply Roman in origin, but they incorporate a small selection of feasts peculiar to Venice (one being the feast of the appearance of Saint Mark, which marked the legendary presentation of Saint Mark's body to the doge in AD 828).[26]

The involvement of music during mass varied in accordance with the rank of the service. Feasts of principal importance in the Roman calendar (Easter, Christmas, Assumption, and so forth) and occasions of local importance (these included the feasts of Saint Mark and Saint Peter Orseolo and the anniversary of the coronation of the incumbent doge) were allocated the best musical resources available to the maestro. On such weighty days the full complement of musicians was in attendance; this could comprise as many as forty choral singers, instrumentalists numbering in excess of thirty (and including players of the bassoon, cornetto, trombone, violin, viola, bass viol, harp, lute, theorbo, and organ), and musicians not on the fixed payroll of the chapel who were hired to bolster numbers and/or to provide extraliturgical entertainment. Polychoral and *concertato* compositions exploited the resonance and spaciousness of the chapel, with musical fragments being passed between groups of musicians placed in different parts of the building. The chapel's organs amplified the musical dialogue: the two main instruments accompanied large choral groupings, while the two *organetti*—portable chamber organs—served smaller ones.[27]

By contrast, the vast majority of masses received considerably more modest musical treatment. Daily (or ferial) High Mass abandoned flamboyant musical forms in favor of the more straightforward a cappella style. As with requiem and vespers music, a cappella settings were performed predominantly from San Marco's octagonal pulpit, known as the *bigonzo* (or *pulpitum magnum*), which stands at the right-hand side of the chapel's rood screen. The music was sung by approximately half the choir (see the "Notes on Performance" below) from a single outsize choirbook placed on a wall-mounted ledge. The process of reducing numbers undoubtedly reflected not only the need to provide respite within the ranks, but also the practical issue that the *bigonzo* could accommodate only about a dozen individuals. The description *ad libitum* on the Organum part for Monferrato's opus 13 gives an indication of the style of accompaniment provided by the sole organist who was in attendance.[28]

The Council of Trent made little impact at San Marco (as was also the case in many other places in Europe).[29] The a cappella performance repertoire of the seventeenth century retained pre-Tridentine items by early Franco-Flemish composers such as Crecquillon, Josquin, Rore, Clemens non Papa, Isaac, and Janequin.[30] Indeed, the tradition of singing Janequin's celebrated *Missa "La bataille"*—a copy of which survives in the ancient music archive of San Marco—on the fifth day of Sexagesima (otherwise known in Venice as Carnival Thursday) continued through Monferrato's era.[31] The performance library was also updated with post-Tridentine items. Monteverdi has been praised for updating a cappella reserves by ordering post-Tridentine masses for four, five, six, and eight voices by Palestrina, Francesco Soriano, Lasso, Gerolamo Lambardi, and Paolo Paciotto. Like succeeding maestros, he supplemented reserves with pastiche compositions, the extant corpus of which is small. This deficiency stems mainly from the fact that maestros tended not to publish "run-of-the-mill" a cappella offerings, unlike up-to-date *concertato* offerings that served to demonstrate compositional prowess. Thus, particular a cappella compositions were available in only very few manuscripts, the quantity of which diminished further with the passing of time. The most serious threat to their survival arrived in 1797 when the ducal chapel was ransacked by Napoleonic forces. Many of the chapel's musical treasures, including Zarlino's concertos for the victory of Lepanto, the first *laude* of Willaert, and precious manuscripts of the Gabrielis, Marcello, Monteverdi, and Carissimi, were looted.[32] As a consequence, important evidence of local liturgical customs was severely depleted. The long ferial mass tradition is represented today by only a smattering of published and unpublished pieces by maestros Monteverdi, Rovetta, Biffi, Lotti, and Monferrato. Monteverdi is, without doubt, the best-known contributor to the corpus by virtue of his published *Messa a 4 da cappella* (*Selva morale e spirituale*, 1641) and *Messa a 4 voci da cappella* (*Messa . . . et salmi*, 1650); however, Monferrato, through the size of his yield, is by far its most prolific contributor.

Monferrato's extant mass music is exclusively a cappella. There are at least eight settings by him: six masses come from his opus 13 *Missae* (1677) and two from his opus 19 *Messe et Magnificat* (1682).[33] One additional a cappella mass, which exists in a nineteenth-century manuscript, has been misattributed to him (as discussed below). Of general interest, opus 13 opens with his longest extant setting; opus 19 concludes with his shortest mass, the aptly titled *Messa breve*; and the concluding setting of opus 13 is the only mass that abandons four vocal parts in favor of a five-voice texture.

Opuses 13 and 19 were intended for use in a sacred choral context. Opus 13 declares its music "Ad usum Cappellarum"; opus 19 is similarly inscribed "Composti Per uso di Capelle." Music from both collections was undeniably performed by the San Marco choir. Late-seventeenth-century choirbooks containing settings from both collections survive in San Marco's collection of ancient choirbooks. One book, originating from 1677, includes the fourth setting in opus 13 along with the opening one in opus 19; another choirbook, this time dating from 1678, contains the five-part mass from opus 13.[34] These *libri da coro* (see plates 8–13) are hugely authoritative sources with regard to both performance procedure at San Marco and dating. In relation to the former point, the grand physical dimensions—detailed in the critical notes—offer physical evidence of the ferial custom of performing music from large books positioned in the *bigonzo*. The dating is interesting in two respects: first, since these books originate from the period 1677–78, they were conceivably consulted by maestro Monferrato himself; second, the fact that the choirbook containing the opus 19 mass is dated 1677 reveals that opus 19 contains material that existed well before its time of publication.

The masses of opuses 13 and 19 are structurally and stylistically representative of the extant a cappella material originating from San Marco in the seventeenth and eighteenth centuries. Monferrato's settings consistently set only the Ordinary of the mass with a single and brief Agnus Dei. To shorten the Agnus Dei was much encouraged at San Marco, for this freed space for extraliturgical items at the offertory. Two further forms of musical abbreviation at San Marco, although not demonstrated here, nevertheless merit mention. The first, which was used specifically on a cappella occasions, entailed the removal of the Benedictus section from the Sanctus; it is an abbreviation that was probably applied occasionally to Monferrato's masses.[35] The second, the quintessentially Venetian procedure of reducing the sung Ordinary to the Kyrie, Gloria, and Credo movements, was a significant contraction aimed at providing extensive extraliturgical space. This action was less well suited to ordinary days, when the *coro* operated with reduced capacity and ceremonial activity was limited.

The arrangement of the mass is typical. The Kyrie is tripartite; the Gloria divides into two parts, its second section beginning "Qui tollis peccata mundi"; the Credo is in three parts, the second and third sections beginning "Et incarnatus est" and "Et in Spiritum Sanctum," respectively; the Sanctus is in two parts, the second beginning "Benedictus qui venit" (and occasionally emphasized with reduced texturing); and the Agnus Dei comprises the single petition, "Agnus Dei, qui tollis peccata mundi: miserere nobis," which is repeated. The usual musical *topoi* make their appearance. In keeping with the typically Renaissance and baroque fondness for allegory, contrasts of meter (sometimes occurring as hemiolas) draw attention to textual features (for instance, Monferrato makes effective use of the hemiola at the opening of the Credo's "Et in Spiritum Sanctum" in opus 13, first mass, mm. 102–5; and opus 13, third mass, mm. 98–104). Most notably, dance-like triple time is applied to triumphal moments in the mass (such as the Credo's "Et resurrexit" and "Et ascendit" texts; see opus 13, second mass, Credo, mm. 82–87; and opus 13, third mass, Credo, mm. 69–73), whereas plaintive moments (such as the lamenting "miserere nobis" in Gloria and Agnus Dei) or words implying physical direction (such as the Credo's "descendit de caelis") sometimes spark rhetorical responses with *mollis* harmonies and/or descending musical shapes (see opus 13, third mass, Gloria, mm. 48–52; opus 13, fourth mass, Gloria, mm. 51–55; and opus 13, third mass, Credo, mm. 44–46). Solemn passages, for instance the litany "Laudamus te. Benedicimus te. Adoramus te. Glorificamus te." in the Gloria, often receive chordal (or homophonic) texturing and clear points of articulation (see opus 13, fourth mass, Gloria, mm. 9–18). Monferrato's motivic content is overly endowed with clichés. Motivic *topoi* include the four-note figure that comprises three rising notes (dotted half note – quarter note – half note) followed by a downward leap (to a half note), which is used so persistently in opus 13 (see the first mass, Kyrie [m. 2] and Gloria [mm. 1 and 3]; the third mass, Kyrie [m. 3]; the fourth mass, Kyrie [mm. 33 and 36], Gloria [m. 2], and Sanctus [m. 35]; the fifth mass, Gloria [m. 1] and Credo [mm. 28, 131, and 135–37]; and the Kyrie II section of the sixth mass, one of several sections from this mass in which the idea occurs), the descending bass figure that precedes the *cadenza perfecta* (see, for example, opus 13, third mass, Kyrie, mm. 45–47; and Credo, mm. 96–98), and a falling imitative pattern that has been identified in other music from the chapel's a cappella repertory (see opus 13, second mass, Kyrie, mm. 43–45; opus 13, third mass, Agnus Dei, mm. 16–19; and opus 13, sixth mass, Agnus Dei, mm. 13–15).[36]

Stylistically, Monferrato acknowledges the traditional association between seicento (and later) a cappella music and the late polyphonic style of the previous century. The retrospective styling, or *stile antico*, is distinct from the "new" *stile concertato*. Whereas masses written in the former style are harmonically self-sufficient and can accordingly be performed with or without instrumental support, those cast in the latter format generally—although not invariably—rely harmonically on continuo support.[37] The point is demonstrated well by opus 19, which omits the continuo part entirely, although this is less an indication of unaccompanied performance than of the fact that the organist normally accompanied in *ad libitum* style (as mentioned above). One further important distinction between the two styles lies in the connection between the *messa concertata* and the seconda prattica—the practice, heavily indebted to Monteverdi and his followers, that served to emphasize the word (*oratio*). The textual responsiveness of concerted masses was facilitated by a new ₵ signature (which introduced an enlarged array of note values), by virtuosic display, by the marked sectionalization of the mass, and by refrain schemes. The latter two features were interrelated: clearly defined sections could be repeated in the form of textual-cum-musical refrain schemata, whereby the repetition of textual *passaggi* invokes reuse of previous musical material. Apart from the fact that refrain structuring improves musical cohesion, a major advantage of the device for composers was the ability to tailor the Ordinary to suit particular liturgical occasions; by this is meant that sections of the mass having relevance to a specific occasion could be repeated and reworked as deemed appropriate.[38]

By contrast, the modus operandi for the *stile antico* mass combined easily performable notation (with narrow tessitura), liturgical multifunctionality, and an awareness of previous compositional procedures (the most obvious being to incorporate the smooth imitative lines that allude to the post-Tridentine Palestrina fashion). It is true that a cappella masses were, like certain concerted masses, associated with particular feasts. Janequin's *Missa "La bataille"* was, as noted, connected with Carnival Thursday, and a *Missa brevis* by Giovanni Rovetta was sung annually on Holy Thursday; however, to reserve particular *stile antico* settings for specific occasions was unsustainable, since the voracious ferial custom necessitated considerable reuse of material.[39] The instruction for ferial occasions was efficient declamation. Rovetta's remarkably short *Missa brevis* provides the ultimate testimony to this requirement at San Marco, but the same trait is perceptible in Monferrato's music. The reluctance to repeat textual material, except where movements end ("in gloria Dei Patris" in the Gloria; "venturi saeculi" in the Credo sections, and so on), may be a by-product of post-Tridentine concerns for ensuring textual clarity by minimizing imitative flurry, but it more likely betrays the procurators' desire to maintain brevity on Ordinary days.[40] Arnold's description of Monferrato's masses as "very austere examples of [the *stile antico* that display] few of the expressive devices of chromaticism and dissonance that other composers used to modify its traditional basis" gives the wrong impression.[41] It is misleading since the northern Italian *stile antico* mass characteristically sidelines seconda prattica expressiveness in favor of businesslike efficiency.

Monferrato was evidently practiced in the late-sixteenth-century art; indeed, although his counterpoint is not always flawless (see opus 13, second mass, Credo, m. 10 [consecutive octaves occurring on the first and third beats of the measure, outer parts]; opus 19, second mass, Kyrie, m. 4 [consecutive octaves on the second and fourth beats, inner parts]; opus 13, fourth mass, Kyrie, m. 10 [parallel fifths on the third and fourth beats, outer parts]; and opus 13, third mass, Sanctus, m. 1 [parallel fifths]), it is nonetheless skillful. He was also fully aware of the need to update, albeit discreetly, the traditional form. His elegant imitative texturing, written in alla breve time, alludes to former compositional practice; however, close inspection reveals the same chordal (or homophonic) construction that shapes the *stile moderno*. The quasi-polyphonic façade is betrayed by succinct harmonic movements (most notably between the tonic and dominant), by the fact that imitative distances are short (see opus 13, fourth mass, Gloria, mm. 21–27; and opus 13, sixth mass, Gloria, mm. 78–79), and by an abundance of homorhythm (see, for example, opus 13, fourth mass, Gloria, mm. 4–6). In a similarly modern vein, the music is tonally developed. Like other late-seventeenth-century compositions, those of Monferrato inhabit a transitional period that bridges cinquecento modality and the fully-fledged tonality that had arrived by the end of the baroque period. The masses can be interpreted tonally: each one has a fixed tonal center (or tonic) with harmonic movements to related areas—the dominant, the subdominant, and the relative minor/major (the latter juxtaposition occurring, for example, in opus 13, fourth mass, Gloria, mm. 63–65 [G minor in mm. 63–64; the relative major, B-flat major, following in m. 65]). Using tonal terminology, opuses 13 and 19 offer collectively six masses in major keys—four in G major (opus 13, the first, third, and fifth masses; and the *Messe breve* of opus 19) and two in F major (opus 13, second and sixth masses)—and two masses in minor keys—one in G minor (opus 13, fourth mass) and the other in D minor (the *Messe a cappella* of opus 19). The sense of tonality is reinforced by the accompanying *organo*, which occasionally breaks away from its role as a *basso seguente*—a line that reproduces the lowest-sounding notation—to reinforce the standard 4–3 progression at points of articulation (see, for example, opus 13, fifth mass, Kyrie, m. 7). Adequate understanding of this music cannot avoid mention of its inherent modality, however. The composer uses two of the most commonly found "key" signatures of the period: one being the void signature with neither flat nor sharp; the other, the flat signature containing B-flat. These signatures are indicative neither of present-day C major / A minor nor of F major / D minor, respectively, but of *cantus durus* and *cantus mollis*—key signatures that operate within the system of church modes, or *tuoni ecclesiastici*, that derive from the diatonic pitches of the three hexachords.[42] Although hexachordal transposition within either signature could achieve far-reaching harmonic effects, Monferrato, working within the confined harmonic space of the *stile antico*, ventures no further than E-flat major in *cantus mollis* and A major in *cantus durus*.

Monferrato's acknowledgment of up-to-date trends is further evident from his incorporation of local traits. The lengthy triple-time passage-work of opus 19, similarly extending in both of its masses from the outset of the Credo to the "Crucifixus," is reminiscent of the coeval *concertato* madrigals, motets, and masses that issued in abundance from Venetian publishers. The leading-note to tonic slurs that lightly pepper the first mass of opus 19 (see the Gloria, mm. 96–97; and Credo, mm. 44–45) may, in fact, originate in the music of Monferrato's close predecessor Monteverdi, in whose music they have been identified by the late Jerome Roche (see example 1).[43] And the harmonic affect at "Gratias" in the second mass of opus 19 (Gloria, mm. 13–14), where two chromatic tutti chords (set a third apart) are juxtaposed, may allude to San Marco's resplendent ceremonial repertory, where this type of chordal chromaticism—albeit used more grandly—occurs with frequency.

Reference has been made to one further a cappella setting, surviving in Venice, which has been misattributed to Monferrato. The existence of this source can be traced to events in the wake of the republic's extinction. Briefly, the looting of San Marco's pre-nineteenth-century music repertory by Napoleon's troops in 1797 awakened the need to preserve its remnants. Maestro Giovanni Agostino Perotti (maestro di cappella from 1811 to 1855) was responsible not just for bringing order to the dismembered archive but for protecting the small corpus by transcribing its contents. His initiative was continued by succeeding maestros, lay clerks, clergy (notably Lorenzo Canal, a late-nineteenth-century canon of San Marco), and members of the Venetian Society of Saint Cecilia. In some cases, it was difficult for individuals to attribute compositions when sources lacked adequate forms of identification. Accordingly, one unidentified four-part a cappella mass, which survives in an early choirbook (of possibly seventeenth-century origins), was misidentified as a work by Monferrato; the true author is, in fact, Gio-

Example 1. Claudio Monteverdi, "Vago augelletto" (*Madrigali guerrieri et amorosi*, 1638), ed. Gianfrancesco Malipiero, vol. 8, part 2 (Vienna: Universal Edition, 1929), concluding measures.

vanni Rovetta. The choirbook, which lacks details of authorship and hefty portions of musical notation, was transcribed in score during the nineteenth century; where there were lacunae, original thematic material was provided by the transcriber. The result is a stylistic hodgepodge, since the interpolated material, written in a post-baroque style, sits incongruously within Rovetta's original content. Criticism aside, this interesting hybrid was performed in San Marco on various occasions, including Holy Thursday.[44]

Masses genuinely authored by Monferrato were also performed at San Marco during the nineteenth century. The three masses that survive in seventeenth-century *libri da coro* (discussed above) were transcribed into modern score and performed alongside *opere classicissime* by other earlier maestros (including Croce, Rovetta, Lotti, and Biffi).[45] Venice was now a very different place: it was blighted by economic hardship and beset by political, social, and cultural change. At San Marco the Cappella Marciana, suffering real economic turmoil, was facing a serious decline in membership; to place this in context, the choir's upper registers were being bolstered by orphaned children from the nearby Orfanotrofio dei Gesuati di Venezia. The continued performance of music by Monferrato and his celebrated contemporaries provided solace to this dejected body of musicians through sustaining a connection with more dignified times.[46] Remarkably, this link remains unbroken: maestros at San Marco continue to ensure the longevity of the chapel's historic works by performing them at regular intervals during the ecclesiastical year.

The masses of Monferrato therefore constitute an important repertory. These are compositions worthy of special distinction, not simply through being relics of an important liturgical practice at one of the most historically important chapels in Europe, but also because they survive as excellent examples of seventeenth-century compositional dexterity. That this music has been performed at San Marco during five centuries is undoubtedly due in some part to its quality, but it also stems from the efforts of generations of maestros, conscious of a need to maintain musical tradition in a basilica buffeted by changing circumstances. Monferrato's masses have become symbols of musical longevity, and they provide testimony to Venice's admirable reluctance to be separated from its past.

The Dedications

Monferrato dedicated the music of opus 13 to the Venetian nobleman Vincenzo (Vicenzo) da Mula (b. 1629).[47] As with other prominent clans in Venice, such as the da Mostos, Morosinis, and Contarinis, the da Mula line—originating from Rome and believed to descend from the Amuli (hence the dual nomenclature da Mula / Amulius)—featured in the major arteries of Venice's hierarchy. The scale of the family's fourteenth-century palazzo, one of the oldest and largest (still surviving) on the Grand Canal, betrays their patrician class. Monferrato, in the typically obsequious style of the time, makes real efforts to preen his dedicatee by acknowledging da Mula's pedigree. The reference to "the praetors' togas" is a likely admission of the family's Roman heritage; and the mention of "the procurators' purple robes" seemingly recalls the great Girolamo da Mula, who was elected procurator of San Marco in 1570 and who functioned as such during the reigns of the Gabrielis. However, Monferrato also ensures that Vincenzo is not outshone by his heritage, and rightfully so: the latter was, after all, worthily upholding the family's authority through not only his membership in the great Council of Ten, the secretive body of senior aristocratic senators who, in effect, ruled the republic,[48] but also through his position as one of the council's three senior figures (*Capi*); da Mula was additionally one of three *Provveditori* assigned charge of Venice's monasteries.[49] In 1682, Doge Alvise Contarini appointed Vincenzo as Captain of Padua,[50] where the family had long-established connections.[51] The name of Vincenzo da Mula unsurprisingly appears as dedicatee on other musical works of the time.[52]

Monferrato dedicated the music of opus 19 to the illustrious Giovanni di Alvise Morosini (1633–82). This Morosini, not to be confused with the late-seventeenth-century doge Giovanni Francesco Morosini, was the Venetian ambassador successively to Charles Emmanuel II of Savoy (1666–68), Louis XIV of France (1668–70), and Leopold I of the Holy Roman Empire (1670–75), and finally the magistrate to Sultan Mehmed IV (1675–80) of the Ottoman Empire. Monferrato makes a direct reference to the last-mentioned appointment through his mention of "Byzantium" (Istanbul); he also alludes to Morosini's wider diplomatic experience. Interestingly, the words "cruelty itself was unable to harbor barbarous feelings" may be an oblique reference to Morosini's celebrated success in persuading Mehmed IV to suppress Turkey's provision of safe havens for Barbary corsairs—a sensitive issue that had stoked Venice's long-standing hostilities with the Turks. On returning to Venice, Morosini assumed the role of procurator of San Marco until his death in 1682.[53]

Notes on Performance

Giovanni Antonio Canal's well-known pen-and-ink illustration of San Marco's interior (see plate 3) shows at least eleven *cantori* singing from one large choirbook—a *libro da coro*—in the chapel's *bigonzo*. It is unclear which service Canal—otherwise known as Canaletto—was actually witnessing here, since daily a cappella masses, requiems, and vespers settings alike were performed from this same *pulpitum*. Confirmable, however, is Canal's depiction of choral size: present-day reenactments by the Cappella Marciana of past choral practices demonstrate that not many more than twelve singers can perform comfortably from the *bigonzo*.[54]

It is unlikely that the reduction of forces on daily occasions was attributable solely to the physical restraints of the *bigonzo*. On those various occasions when the choir sang *messe a cappella* at other Venetian churches, forces were similarly reduced.[55] On 8 January, for instance, some members of the choir sang at San Pietro di Castello—Venice's cathedral until 1816—while others remained at San Marco,[56] and precisely half the choir sang at San Zorzi on 26 December while the other half sang the same mass on home ground. Although the method for selection is unclear, it is reasonable to assume that some form of rotation was operating (as occurred with the chapel's two organists, who rotated on a weekly basis). Certainly, on some circumstances, the maestro handpicked his singers, as happened on 1 May, when he chose the same group of singers to sing an a cappella setting at San Marco, later repeated at Santi Filippo e Giacomo.

While the *bigonzo* was the usual venue for *messe a cappella* at San Marco, occasional deviations from this custom occurred. On 16 May the upper terraces of the building—usually reserved for *messe solenne*—were used in honor of the attending doge. Later on the same day, following the departure of the doge, an a cappella mass was performed from the *bigonzo* for the hoi polloi. And on both 29 August and 28 December the *messa a cappella* was sung from the baptistry of the chapel, whereas on 16 May it came from the Cappella del Santo.

Monferrato consistently includes an Agnus Dei movement with only two petitions. This feature, commonplace in mass music of this era (and rarely discussed by scholars), requires some attention if the music is to be performed in a strict liturgical fashion. The complete text of the Agnus Dei comprises the following three petitions:

> Agnus Dei, qui tollis peccata mundi: miserere nobis.
> Agnus Dei, qui tollis peccata mundi: miserere nobis.
> Agnus Dei, qui tollis peccata mundi: dona nobis pacem.

Monferrato's omission of the supplication "dona nobis pacem" is not indicative of earlier performance practice either at San Marco or elsewhere. Although the "dona nobis pacem" was commonly omitted throughout Europe on Holy Thursday (an act prescribed in the Roman Rite to express detestation at the traitorous kiss of Judas), it was otherwise normally included, either by the celebrant (after the movement concluded) or by the choir—procedures that were, and continue to be, practiced in the Roman Rite. When sung by the choir, the singers simply repeat the entire movement (as many times as necessary) until the Fraction—the breaking of the Eucharistic bread—reaches its conclusion, at which point the words "dona nobis pacem" are substituted for the final invocation of "miserere nobis." So if the movement is to be sung without repetition, the substitution is made at the first opportunity.[57]

Finally, Monferrato's prints—typically for their time—contain no written performance directions regarding tempi and dynamics; both matters have, accordingly, been left entirely to the judgment of performers. Undoubtedly, an effective tempo responds not only to the musical text, but also to the type of ensemble and its performance location. Critically, the minim of the *stile antico* mass retains its inherited meaning as the *minima nota* (or smallest note). The danger, however, lies in taking the minim at such a pace that the music loses dignity; indeed, a slower speed is implied by Monferrato's consistent use of the *proportio sesquialtera* $\frac{3}{2}$ in triple-time sections. This proportional signature—not to be confused with three minims per measure—indicates that three semibreves correspond to two units of pulse, one unit being traditionally measured by the semibreve, whereas the *proportio tripla* $\frac{3}{1}$ (commonly used in coeval *concertato* and *stile antico* music) implies swifter movement. In the edition, proportional relationships have been shown above relevant measures with equations. Importantly, these act merely as suggestions, since performance treatises from Monferrato's time are inconsistent: whereas some advocate strictness of the principal beat at points of metrical juncture, others encourage flexibility. The performer should not become inhibited by this issue, since, in practice, it is likely that even seasoned contemporary performers were liable to unintentional metrical waywardness.[58] With regard to dynamic levels, these are essentially incorporated in the music through Monferrato's ever-changing textural combinations; in short, the transparent closely-imitative ideas, which provide intimate sonorities, provide respite from the louder fully-textured chordal sections.

Notes

The following sigla are cited in the notes:

I-Vas   Venice, Archivio di Stato
I-Vnm   Venice, Biblioteca Nazionale Marciana
I-Vsm   Venice, Procuratoria di San Marco

1. Nadal is a North Italian dialectal form of the name Natale; the latter is reflective of Tuscanization.

2. This information comes from Monferrato's obituary in I-Vas, Necrologio of the Provveditori alla Sanità, registro 894, entry for 13 April 1685. The document places Monferrato's birth at some time during 1609–10. The year 1603 is offered in Francesco Caffi, *Storia della musica sacra nella già cappella ducale di S. Marco in Venezia dal 1318 al 1797*, ed. Elvidio Surian (Milan, 1931; repr., Florence: L. S. Olschki, 1987), 231. A birth date of ca. 1615 is given by Denis Arnold in *The New Grove Dictionary of Music and Musicians*, 2nd ed. (hereafter *NG2*), s.v. "Monferrato, Natale."

3. Monferrato's oeuvre reveals a preference for the sacred as opposed to the secular style. In this respect, he falls outside the brand of "secularized" priests, prevalent in the period following the Council of Trent, discussed in Francis Burkley, "Priest-Composers of the Baroque: A Sacred-Secular Conflict," *Musical Quarterly* 54 (1968): 169–84.

4. Monteverdi commends the benefits of ducal employment in his letter to Alessandro Striggio of 1620, quoted in Paolo Fabbri, *Monteverdi*, trans. Tim Carter (Cambridge: Cambridge University Press, 1994), 131.

5. The competition for the organist post is described in James H. Moore, *Vespers at St. Mark's: Music of Alessandro Grandi, Giovanni Rovetta, and Francesco Cavalli*, 2 vols. (Ann Arbor: UMI Research Press, 1981), 1:19; and in Fabbri, *Monteverdi*, 130–31. The information on Monferrato's employment as cantor comes from I-Vas, Decreti e Terminazioni della Procuratia de Supra, Collezione degli Atti della Procuratia, registro 144, fols. 38r and 132r–v.

6. I-Vas, Decreti e Terminazioni della Procuratia de Supra, Collezione degli Atti della Procuratia, registro 144, fol. 272r.

7. See Giovanni Rovetta, *Masses*, ed. Jonathan R. J. Drennan, Recent Researches in the Music of the Baroque Era, vol. 146 (Middleton, Wis.: A-R Editions, 2006), ix.

8. A comprehensive list of the chapel's music staff (with salary details) is given in Eleanor Selfridge-Field, *Venetian Instrumental Music from Gabrieli to Vivaldi* (New York: Dover Publications, 1994), 330–48.

9. For a precise description of the Mendicanti's population, see Michael Talbot, *Benedetto Vinaccesi: A Musician in Brescia and Venice in the Age of Corelli* (Oxford: Clarendon Press, 1994), 54–55.

10. Quoted from M. V. Constable, "The Venetian 'Figlie del Coro': Their Environment and Achievement," *Music and Letters* 63 (1982): 194–95.

11. See Moore, *Vespers at St. Mark's*, 1:92–94.

12. It has been assumed that Monferrato lost to Cavalli in the ballot for the position. However, the procurators' minute books make no reference to any application by Monferrato.

13. See Moore, *Vespers at St. Mark's*, 1:95–96.

14. Monferrato complained in 1677 of a lack of excellent high voices: "ne soprani, ne castrati esquisiti . . ." See Olga Termini, "Singers at San Marco in Venice: The Competition between Church and Theatre (*c*1675–*c*1725)," *Royal Musical Association Research Chronicle* 17 (1981): 67.

15. The entries in the procurators' minute books, from which this information was gleaned, are transcribed (occasionally in abridged form) in Francesco Passadore and Franco Rossi, *San Marco: Vitalità di una tradizione*, 4 vols. (Venice: Edizioni

Fondazione Levi, 1994), 1:275–77. Importantly, the *prove* occurred on 20 April (not 10 April, as given in Moore, *Vespers at St. Mark's,* 1:96). Alessandro Contarini, the chapel's treasurer, was critical of Monferrato's measures, claiming they were sowing confusion among the singers.

16. This information comes partly from Gabriele Fantoni, *N. Monferrato e G. F. Brusa, veneziani maestri di musica* (Venice: Edizioni Ricordi, 1876), 7–8. Fantoni's brief monograph is preserved in I-Vnm, Misc. C 0000 3494; it was reissued as the article "Scoperta e ricupero di musiche autografe ed inedite dei veneziani maestri N. Monferrato e G. F. Brusa," *Gazzetta musicale di Milano* 32 (1877): 147–68, and later as an independent publication, *Scoperta e ricupero di musiche autografe ed inedite dei veneziani maestri Natale Monferrato e Gian Francesco Brusa e cenni d'illustrazione e di ratifica alle memorie di questi ed altri musicisti loro contemporanei* (Milan: Edizioni Ricordi, [ca. 1890]); the latter is preserved in I-Vnm, Misc. B 0000 8490. The information on musicians' payments comes from Passadore and Rossi, *San Marco,* 1:479–83.

17. Monferrato's connection with Sala is explained in Richard A. McGowan, "The Venetian Printer Giuseppe Sala: New Information Based upon Archival Documents," *Fontes Artis Musicae* 36 (1989): 102–8. Although Monferrato left the family home to reside in the *canonica* of San Marco, his relatives likely remained in the family dwelling. This was standard procedure for the time, and, even in modern-day Venice, some families uphold centuries-old occupations of particular residences.

18. The dating of Monferrato's opuses 18 and 19 is discussed further below (see note 33).

19. The procurators' entry detailing Monferrato's medallion is transcribed in Passadore and Rossi, *San Marco,* 1:282.

20. Monferrato's obituary is cited in note 2 above. His setting of *De profundis* (Psalm 129) was also performed during the service; sources of the latter are preserved in I-Vsm, B.810/1–28. The Rovetta requiem is newly edited and published in Rovetta, *Masses,* ed. Drennan.

21. To judge from records at San Marco, Volpe was the first regularly paid player of the *spinetta* during Holy Week. The systematic integration of this keyboard instrument began during Monferrato's tenure; see Eleanor Selfridge-Field, "Rovetta's Music for Holy Week," in *La cappella musicale di San Marco nell'età moderna: Atti del convegno internazionale di studi, Venezia, Palazzo Giustinian Lolin, 5–7 settembre 1994,* ed. Francesco Passadore and Franco Rossi (Venice: Fondazione Levi, 1998), 412–15.

22. The commemorative services, which were funded by Monferrato, ended well before the nineteenth century. The nineteenth-century Venetian historian Gabriele Fantoni indicates that the annual performances of Rovetta's requiem at San Marco, San Silvestro, and San Bartolomeo had long since disappeared by the mid-nineteenth century (see *N. Monferrato e G. F. Brusa*). The tradition at San Marco may have survived into the eighteenth century; a requiem by Rovetta is cited in the 1720 inventory of music provided by Francesco Caffi (see *Storia della musica,* 444). Regarding San Bartolomeo, the fact that the surviving partbooks of *De profundis* (cited in note 20 above) are dated 1746/47 may signify that the Rovetta requiem was still in the repertory at that time.

23. In Ireland, for example, the core of the Roman liturgy was retained, but the missal was supplemented with feasts for local saints: Saint Munchin, Saint Ita, Saint Mel, and so forth. The process of modifying the core liturgy to suit the customs and beliefs of particular provinces continues to function in Roman Catholic (and indeed Anglican) churches of the present day.

24. Recent research on this matter is included in Jonathan R. J. Drennan, "Giovanni Rovetta's 'Missa brevis': A Symbol of Musical Longevity," *Recercare* 22 (2010): 111–46.

25. See ibid., 122–24.

26. See Rovetta, *Masses,* ed. Drennan, x.

27. Copious information is available on these practices. See, for example: Fabbri, *Monteverdi,* 128–29; Drennan, "Giovanni Rovetta's 'Missa brevis' "; Rovetta, *Masses,* ed. Drennan; Jonathan R. J. Drennan, "Another Mass Attributable to Giovanni Rovetta," *Music and Letters* 88 (2007): 597 n. 37; and Moore, *Vespers at St. Mark's,* 1:81–110. James H. Moore's "*Venezia favorita da Maria:* Music for the Madonna Nicopeia and Santa Maria della Salute," *Journal of the American Musicological Society* 37 (1984): 299–355, gives a comprehensive insight into specific customs and ceremonies. The latter article is reappraised in Jeffrey G. Kurtzman, "Monteverdi's 'Mass of Thanksgiving' Revisited," *Early Music* 22 (1994): 63–84.

28. See Drennan, "Giovanni Rovetta's 'Missa brevis,' " 116–17.

29. See Craig A. Monson, "The Council of Trent Revisited," *Journal of the American Musicological Society* 55 (2002): 1–37. See also Drennan, "Giovanni Rovetta's 'Missa brevis,' " 119–20.

30. Moore, *Vespers at St. Mark's,* 1:85–86.

31. Both the performance of the Janequin mass (during Cavalli's tenure, when Monferrato served as vice-maestro) and its choirbook, from which the Cappella Marciana sang, are discussed in Jonathan Drennan, "Attributions to Giovanni Rovetta," *Early Music* 33 (2005): 413–22.

32. Drennan, "Giovanni Rovetta's 'Missa brevis,' " 130–31.

33. Monferrato's opus 19 is dated 1681; however, to judge from the year of publication of opus 18, 1682 is likely to be the year when opus 19 was published. Opus 18 was issued either very late in 1681 or early in 1682—the procurators of San Marco officially acknowledged its existence on 11 January 1682, probably motivated by Monferrato's dedication of it to them (in return for which they presented him with a medallion, as discussed above). So the likelihood is that opus 19 came out shortly afterward, in which case 1681 is to be understood *more veneto*: a term denoting the fact that in Venice the year advanced on 1 March; thus 1 January 1681 *more veneto* is equivalent to 1 January 1682 according to our modern reckoning.

34. The large ancient choirbooks of the Cappella Marciana are cataloged in Passadore and Rossi, *San Marco,* 4:1479–1503. Monferrato's masses in choirbook format are cataloged there as 1930/i, 1929, and 1930/ii, respectively.

35. See Drennan, "Attributions to Rovetta," 415–20.

36. This idea is commented upon in Drennan, "Attributions to Rovetta," and in Rovetta, *Masses,* ed. Drennan.

37. *Concertati* may comprise, either solely or partially, textures that are harmonically self-sufficient. Intended for group as opposed to solo performance, vocally self-sufficient textures could receive instrumental backing; they are generally labelled *da cappella*.

38. The refrain form is described in depth in Jonathan R. J. Drennan, "The Masses of Giovanni Rovetta," 2 vols. (Ph.D. diss., University of Ulster, 2002).

39. See Fabbri, *Monteverdi,* 132; and Drennan, "Attributions to Rovetta."

40. See Moore, *Vespers at St. Mark's,* 1:85. Rovetta's *Missa brevis*—discussed in Drennan, "Giovanni Rovetta's 'Missa brevis' "—is the ultimate testimony to this principle.

41. See *NG2*, "Monferrato."

42. Monferrato's music conforms to the system of eight church modes discussed by Adriano Banchieri (1567–1634) in his treatise *L'organo suonarino* (Venice, 1605), published in facsimile with an introduction by Giulio Cattin (Amsterdam: Frits Knuf, 1969). Monferrato states clearly his incorporation of church tones one through six in the Magnificat settings that follow the masses of opus 19. There is relevant information in Joel Lester, *Between Modes and Keys: German Theory 1592–1802* (Stuyvesant, N.Y.: Pendragon Press, 1989), 77–78; and in Eric Chafe, *Monteverdi's Tonal Language* (New York: Schirmer, 1992).

43. See also Jerome Roche, *North Italian Church Music in the Age of Monteverdi* (Oxford: Clarendon Press, 1984), 70.

44. See Drennan, "Another Mass Attributable to Rovetta," 596–603.

45. Passadore and Rossi provide a comprehensive overview of key events in San Marco's history in *San Marco,* vol. 1.

46. See Drennan, "Giovanni Rovetta's 'Missa brevis,' " 121–30.

47. Vicenzo da Mula's date of birth is given in Pier Cesare Ioly Zorattini, ed., *Processi del S. Ufficio di Venezia contro ebrei e giudaizzanti, 1682–1734* (Florence: Leo S. Olschki, 1994), 75. Research on his life (including the time of his death) is work in progress by the author.

48. Vincenzo da Mula is mentioned in this capacity in 1685. See Claire Fontijn, *Desperate Measures: The Life and Music of Antonia Padoani Bembo* (Oxford: Oxford University Press, 2006), 51.

49. Isidoro Gatti, *Il P. Vincenzo Coronelli dei Frati Minori Conventuali negli anni del generalato (1701–1707)*, pt. 1 (Rome: Pontificia Università Gregoriana, 1976), 816.

50. *Podestaria e Capitanato di Padova*, ed. Amelio Tagliaferri (Milan: Dott. A. Giuffrè Editore, 1975), lv.

51. The Collegio Amulio and Compagnia del gran nome di Dio were founded in Prato della Valle, Padua (to assist the orphans and the children of the poor) by Cardinal Marc'Antonio da Mula during the previous century; see Eleanor Selfridge-Field, *A New Chronology of Venetian Opera and Related Genres, 1660–1760* (Stanford: Stanford University Press, 2007), 188.

52. Leone Allacci, *Drammaturgia di Lione Allacci: Accresciuta e continuata fino all'anno MDCCLV* (Venice: Presso G. Pasquali, 1755), 421.

53. There is copious literature dealing with Morosini that includes his dealings with the Turks. See, for example, Kenneth Meyer Setton, *Venice, Austria, and the Turks in the Seventeenth Century* (Philadelphia: American Philosophical Society, 1991), 256. Setton provides a brief account of Morosini's challenging time in Istanbul. Much greater detail is available in Nicolo Barozzi and Guglielmo Berchet, eds., *Le relazioni degli stati Europei lette al senato dagli ambasciatori Veneti nel secolo decimosettimo*, series 3, Italia, vol. 1, Torino (Venice, 1862), 379–82, and series 5, Turchia, vol. 2 (Venice, 1872), 197–248.

54. I learned this from private correspondence with maestro Gemmani during 2011.

55. The information that follows comes from a source entitled *Tavola*, which is an ecclesiastical calendar dated 1761 that communicates the daily duties of San Marco's musicians. Its rubrics likely relate to previous eras; see Drennan, "Attributions to Rovetta," 421–22 n. 18. The information on music given in the *Tavola* accords with that in the two great *Cerimoniali* of San Marco: those of Bartolomeo Bonifacio (whose version dates from 1564) and Giovanni Pace (whose version dates from 1678). There is additional relevant information on these sources in Drennan, "Giovanni Rovetta's 'Missa brevis,'" 116–24.

56. The same procedure pertained on 15 June (at San Vito), 26 June (at Santi Giovanni e Paolo), and 7 October (at San Giustina).

57. This matter is discussed in greater detail in Drennan, "Giovanni Rovetta's 'Missa brevis,'" 140–43.

58. Relevant discussion of these matters occurs in Jeffrey Kurtzman, *The Monteverdi Vespers of 1610: Music, Context, Performance* (Oxford: Clarendon Press, 1999), 433–66.

Plate 1. Monferrato's bust, located above the door in the sacristy of the church of San Bartolomeo, Venice. Beneath the bust is carved the following inscription, which is transcribed in Francesco Caffi, *Storia della musica sacra nella già cappella ducale di S. Marco in Venezia dal 1318 al 1797*, ed. Elvidio Surian (Florence: L. S. Olschki, 1987), 234: "Utitur hic aspectu pro voce A[uctore] R[everendissimo] D[omino] Natalis Monferratus inter musicos ducalis Basilicae choros protomagister, hujus autem Ecclesiae presbyter vere primus, comitate, gravitate, beneficentia, qui studuit hac in imagine semper videri superstes ut numquam, vel de marmore, amoris sui dulcia pignora silvisset." (Here Author and Reverend Lord Natale Monferrato uses his facial expression as his voice: maestro di cappella amongst the music-making choirs of the ducal basilica, and truly the priest of this church foremost in graciousness, dignity, and beneficence, who strove in this representation [on the bust] always to be seen as surviving, so that never, even [speaking] from the marble, would he keep quiet about the sweet pledges of his love.) Translation by J. D. Cullington. Photograph by the editor.

Plate 2. Monferrato's tomb, located by the door of the sacristy in the church of San Bartolomeo, Venice. The inscription on the tomb—now predominantly illegible—is transcribed in complete form in Francesco Caffi, *Storia della musica sacra nella già cappella ducale di S. Marco in Venezia dal 1318 al 1797*, ed. Elvidio Surian (Florence: L. S. Olschki, 1987), 234: "Protomystae musicaeque praefecti mortuali sub lapide silentis saxeum mne[m]osynon cujus propr[i]e innumeras virtutes oris hilaritatem amplitudinem animi morum suaveolentiam urbi deoque consonam retegit caelatus affabre lapis: illius inquam qui cum ecclesiae suae alumnos pluribus donavit titulis jure recensendum censeas ex ipsissima divi Bartholamaei agnatione: vivens enim opibus decorticari passus quo sacris ritibus numerosius vacetur: ergo pientissimo auctori immo parenti optime merito Natali Monferrato aurea coelorum saecula aeternumque vale parentent posteri omnes." (A memorial in stone of the leading priest and director of music lying silent beneath the funerary slab, whose especially innumerable virtues—joyousness of speech, breadth of mind, and a fragrance of character in harmony with the city and with God—the cleverly carved stone reveals: of him, I say, who, as he rewarded the pupils belonging to his church with very many titles, you would think ought justly to be counted as from the very same stock as godly Bartholomew's: for when he lived he suffered being stripped of his wealth so that there might be more abundant opportunity for religious ceremonies. Therefore to Natale Monferrato, a most pious originator—or, rather, parent—of such excellent merits, let all posterity gratefully offer the golden ages of heaven and an eternal farewell.) Translation by J. D. Cullington. Photograph by the editor.

Plate 3. Giovanni Antonio Canal's vivid depiction of the interior of San Marco (1766), looking from the south transept. Illustration courtesy of the Kunsthalle, Hamburg.

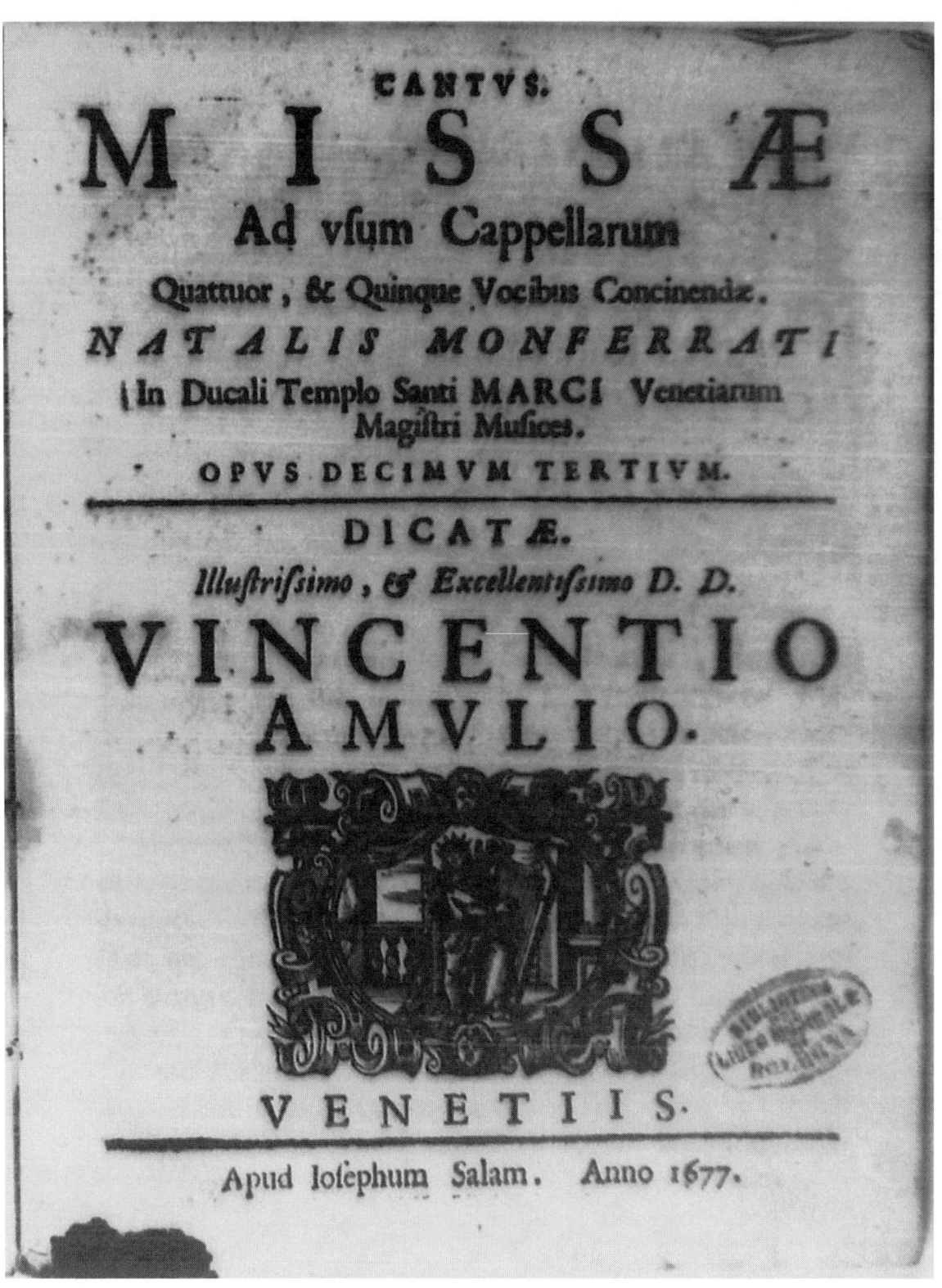

Plate 4. Natale Monferrato, *Missae,* Op. 13 (Venice: Sala, 1677), title page of collection, Canto partbook. Courtesy of the Museo internazionale e biblioteca della musica di Bologna.

Plate 5. Natale Monferrato, *Missae,* Op. 13 (Venice: Sala, 1677), first page of music from collection, Canto partbook. Courtesy of the Museo internazionale e biblioteca della musica di Bologna.

Plate 6. Natale Monferrato, *Messe et Magnificat,* Op. 19 (Venice: Sala, 1682 [1681 *more veneto*—according to the Venetian calendar]), title page of collection, Canto partbook. Courtesy of the Bibliothèque nationale de France, Paris.

Plate 7. Natale Monferrato, *Messe et Magnificat*, Op. 19 (Venice: Sala, 1682 [1681 *more veneto*]), first page of music from collection, Canto partbook. Courtesy of the Bibliothèque nationale de France, Paris.

Plate 8. Title page from a seventeenth-century *libro da coro* of the Cappella Marciana containing Monferrato's *Missa quat[t]uor vocibus*. The same composition is published as *Missa prima* in the composer's opus 19 (1682); in this edition it is titled *Messa a cappella*. Folio reproduced courtesy of the Procuratoria di San Marco, Venice.

Plate 9. Opening page of music from a seventeenth-century *libro da coro* of the Cappella Marciana containing Monferrato's *Missa quat[t]uor vocibus*. The same composition is published as *Missa prima* in the composer's opus 19 (1682); in this edition it is titled *Messa a cappella*. Folio reproduced courtesy of the Procuratoria di San Marco, Venice.

Plate 10. Title page from a seventeenth-century *libro da coro* of the Cappella Marciana containing Monferrato's *Missa quat[t]uor vocibus*. The same composition is published as *Messa quarta* in the composer's opus 13 (1677); in this edition it is titled *Messa a cappella quarta*. This mass is bound together with (and follows) the opus 19 mass illustrated by plates 8 and 9. Folio reproduced courtesy of the Procuratoria di San Marco, Venice.

Plate 11. Opening page of music from a seventeenth-century *libro da coro* of the Cappella Marciana containing Monferrato's *Missa quat[t]uor vocibus*. The same composition is published as *Messa quarta* in the composer's opus 13 (1677); in this edition it is titled *Messa a cappella quarta*. Folio reproduced courtesy of the Procuratoria di San Marco, Venice.

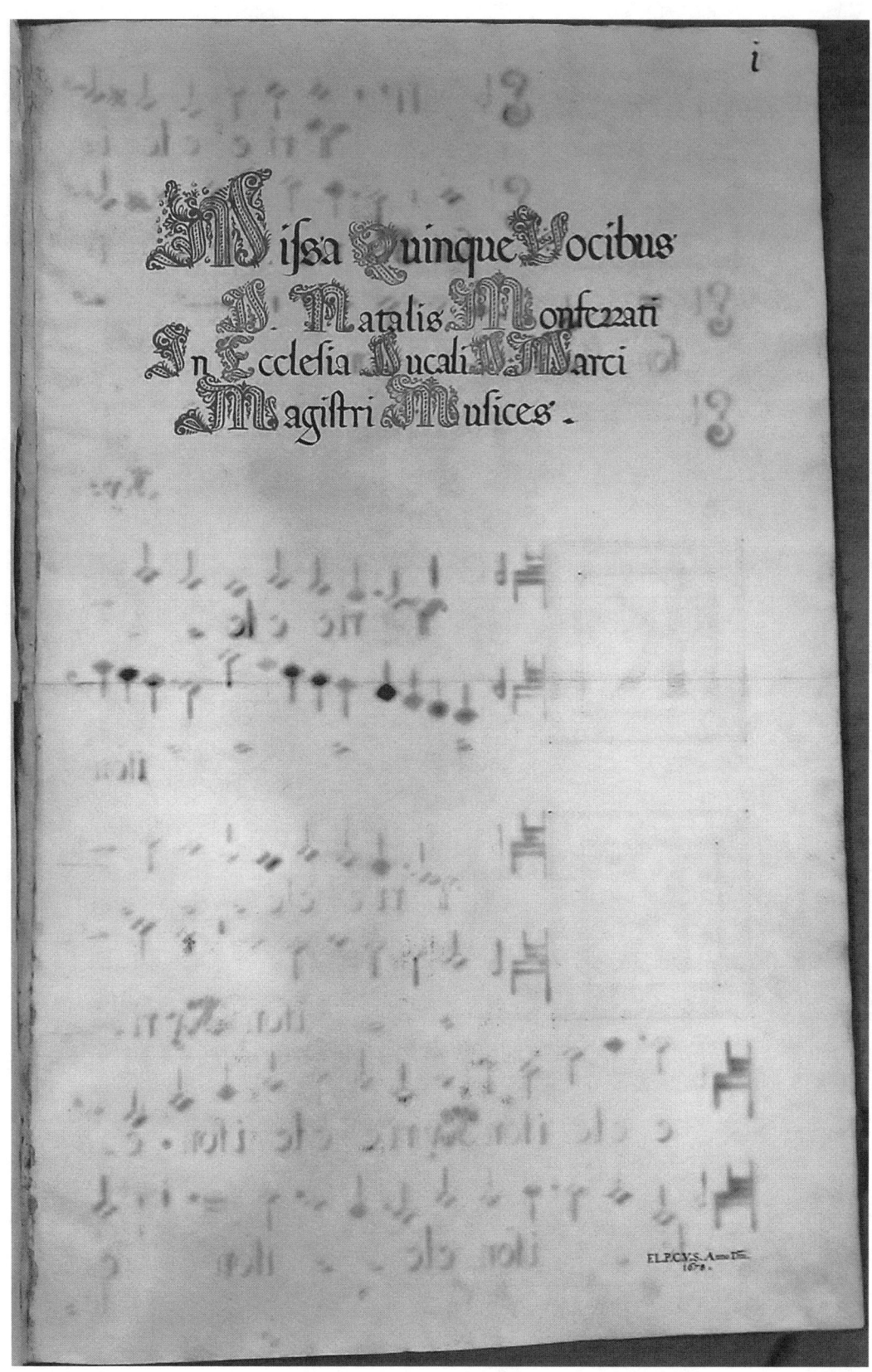

Plate 12. Title page from a seventeenth-century *libro da coro* of the Cappella Marciana containing Monferrato's *Missa quinque vocibus*. The same composition is published as *Messa sesta* in the composer's opus 13 (1677); in this edition it is titled *Messa a cappella sesta*. Folio reproduced courtesy of the Procuratoria di San Marco, Venice.

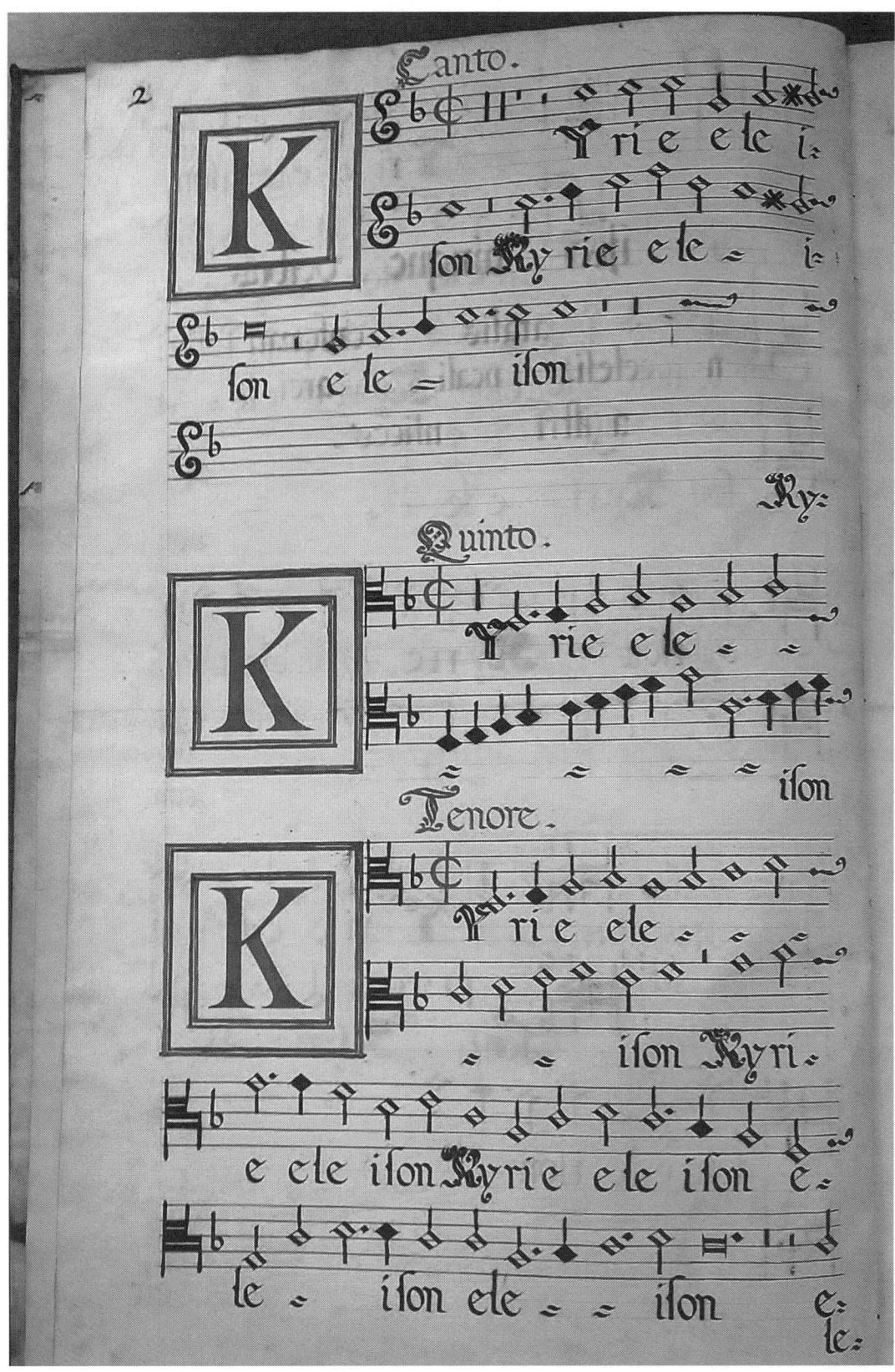

Plate 13. Opening page of music from a seventeenth-century *libro da coro* of the Cappella Marciana containing Monferrato's *Missa quinque vocibus*. The same composition is published as *Messa sesta* in the composer's opus 13 (1677); in this edition it is titled *Messa a cappella sesta*. Folio reproduced courtesy of the Procuratoria di San Marco, Venice.

Missae, ad usum cappellarum, quattuor & quinque vocibus concinendae, Op. 13

Dedication

Provveditor Generale
Illustrissimo et Excellentissimo D[at] D[edicat]
VINCENTIUS AMULIUS
Senatori Amplissimo
NATALIS MONFERRATUS.
F[eliciter]

Non mihi debes, sed humanitati virtutique tuae, Illustrissime et Excellentissime Mecoenas, quod sacrum proni in obsequium mei tibi se deuoueant hi musici labores. Cogitanti enim mihi priùs quàm eos in lucem ederem, cuiusnam muniendi essent praesidio, tu optatò solus antè alios aduenisti. Et sanè, quis eos benigniore fulturus est et decoraturus patrocinio quàm Tu, qui egregium Amuliae Familiae Theatrum, quod pietas virtutis Parens reclusit, Europa ornauit, Orbis miratus est, Vnus adimples. Nec vacat in praesentia maiorum tuorum aut Purpuras Procuratorias aut Praetorias Togas aut militaria Saga commemorare. Tibi enim à Proauis tuis non degeneri, haùd necessè est ab illis laudes emendicare, ut fulgeas. Venetam quippè maiestatem eo decore sustines priuatè, quo publicè meliùs sustinere promereris in Throno. Vectigalem ergò agnoscens animum, quem deuouent, dùm tibi aduoluuntur hi musici concentus, eos excipias arridenti fronte, exceptosque sinù benignè foueas. Quod si eis, ut sperò, euenerit, plùs vertetur crimini nunc usquè latuisse, quàm erupisse modò temeritati. Vale.

To the General Magistrate [a title exercised by Venetian nobles in the service of their government], the Most Illustrious and Excellent VINCENZO DA MULA, Most Eminent Senator, NATALE MONFERRATO happily gives and dedicates this.

You owe it not to me, but to your own humaneness and virtue, most illustrious and excellent Maecenas, that these musical labors of mine pledge themselves to you, eager to pay you sacred obedience. For as I pondered, before I could bring them into the light, by whose assistance they ought to be strengthened, you alone before any others came in answer to my prayer. And surely, who is likely to support and enhance them with kinder patronage than you, who on your own fill the da Mula family's public stage, which piety—the parent of virtue—opened up, Europe adorned, and the world admired? Nor is there leisure at present to call to mind either the procurators' purple robes or the praetors' togas or the military cloaks of your ancestors. For you, who are by no means inferior to your forebears, do not need to scrounge praises from them in order to shine. Indeed, you uphold the majesty of Venice with the same distinction in private as that with which you deserve to uphold it, better still, in public on the throne. Acknowledging, therefore, the productive mind which these musical harmonies pledge as they prostrate themselves before you, may you receive them with a smiling countenance and, having received them, caress them kindly in your bosom. If, as I hope, that does happen to them, it will be interpreted as blameworthy that they have lain hidden until now rather than as presumptuous that they have just now burst forth. Farewell.

Translation by J. D. Cullington

Messa a cappella prima

Kyrie

17
Chri- ste e- le- i- son, e- le- i- son, e- le- - i-
Chri- ste e- le- i- son, e- le- i- son, e- le- - i-
Chri- ste e- le- i-
6 [6] 5 6
23
-son, Chri- ste e- le- i- son, e- le- i-
-son, e- le- - i- son,
Chri- ste e- le- i- son, e- le- i- son, e-
-son, e- le- i- son, e- le- i- son, Chri- ste e- le- i- son, e-
6 7 6
28
-son, Chri- ste e- le- i- son, e- - le- i-
Chri- ste e- le- i- son, e- le- i-
-le- - i- son,
-le- - i- son, e- le- i- son, Chri-
6 4 3 4 3 9 8 7 6 4 3

33
-son, Chri- - ste e- - le- - i- son.
-son, Chri- ste e- - le- i- son, Chri- ste e- le- i- son.
Chri- ste e- le- i- son, Chri- ste e- le- i- son.
-ste e- le- i- son, Chri- ste e- le- - i- son.
6 [6] 4 [♯]3 5 7 [♯]6
39
Ky- ri- e
Ky- ri- e e- le- i- son, e- le-
Ky- ri- e e- le- i- son, e- le- i- son,
Ky- ri- e e- le- i- son, e- le- i- son, Ky- ri-
6 4 [♯]3
44
e- le- i- son, e- le- i- son,
- - i- son, e- le- i- son, Ky- ri- e
Ky- ri- e e- le- i- son, e- le- i- son, Ky- ri-
-e e- le- i- son, e- le- i- son, e- le- i- son,
4 [♯]3

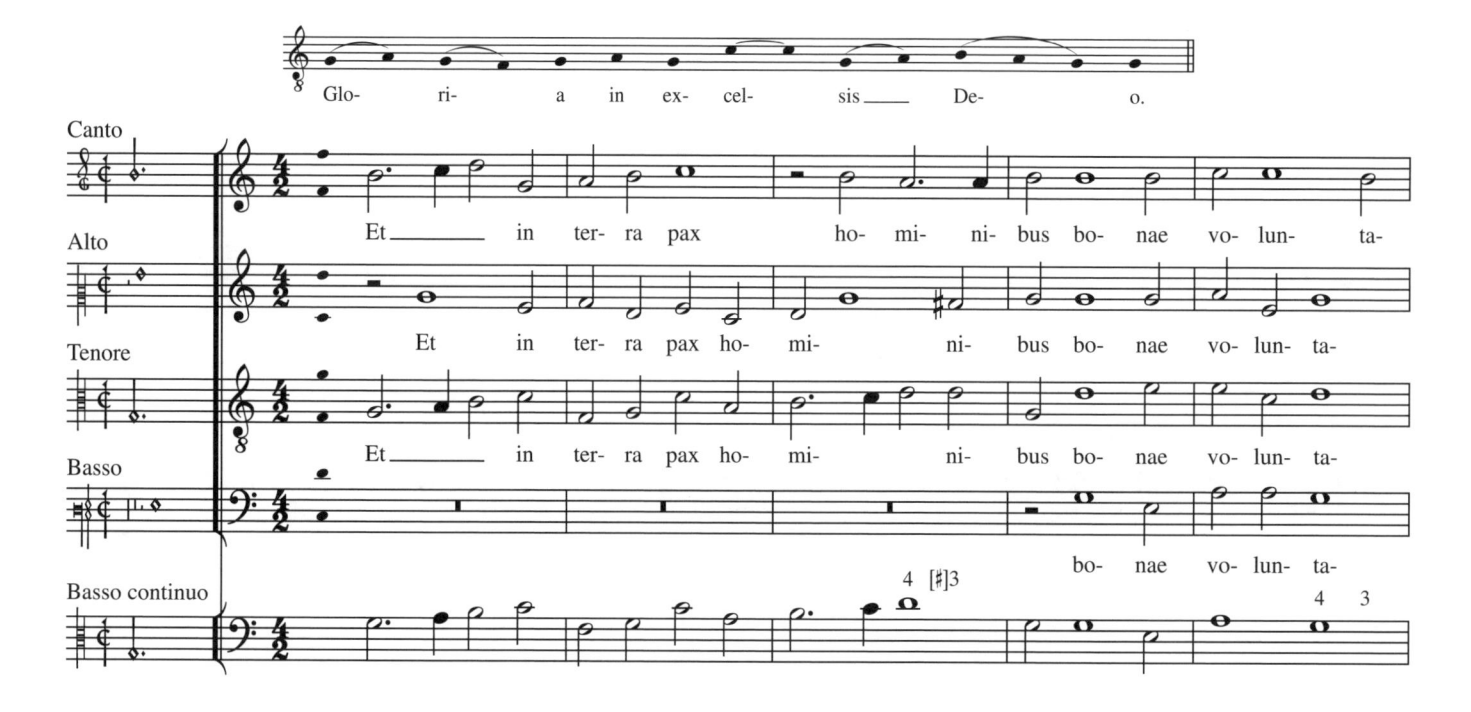

Gloria

6
-tis. Lau- da- - mus te. Be- ne- di- ci-mus te. Ad- o- ra- - mus te.
-tis. Lau- da- mus te. Be- ne- di- ci- mus te. Ad- o- ra- mus te.
-tis. Lau- da- mus te. Be- ne- di- ci- mus te. Ad- o- ra- - mus te. Glo-
-tis. Lau- da- mus te. Be- ne- di- ci- mus te. Ad- o- ra- mus te.
12
Glo- ri- fi- ca- - mus te. Gra- ti-
Glo- ri- fi- ca- - mus te, glo- ri- fi- ca- mus te. Gra- ti-
-ri- fi- ca- - mus te, glo- ri- fi- ca- - mus te. Gra- ti-
Glo- ri- fi- ca- - mus te, glo- ri- fi- ca- - mus te. Gra- ti-
18
-as a- gi- mus ti- bi pro-
-as a- gi- mus ti- - bi pro- pter ma- gnam
-as a- gi- mus ti- bi pro- pter ma-gnam glo- ri- am,
-as a- gi- mus ti- - bi pro- pter ma- - gnam glo- ri- am, glo- ri- am

24
- pter ma-gnam glo- ri- am, glo- ri- am tu- am. Do- mi- ne De- us,
glo- ri- am, pro- pter ma-gnam glo- ri- am tu- am. Do- mi- ne De- us,
pro- pter ma- - gnam glo- ri- am tu- am. Do- mi- ne De- - us, Rex
tu- am. Do- mi- ne De- - us,
7 6 5 7 6 4 ♯ 4 [♯]3
30
Rex cae- le- - stis, De- - us Pa- ter om-
Rex cae- le- - stis,
cae- le- - - stis, De- - us Pa- ter om- ni-
Rex cae- le- - - stis, De- us Pa- ter om-
4 3 ♯ 6
35
-ni- po- tens. Do- - mi- ne Fi- li u- ni- ge- ni- te Je- su
Do- - mi- ne Fi- li u- ni- ge- ni- te Je-
- po- tens. u- ni- ge- ni- te Je- su
-ni- po- tens. Do- mi- ne Fi- - li u- ni- ge- ni- te Je-
4 [♯]3 ♯ 4 [♯]3

41
Chri- ste. Do- - - - mi-
- su Chri- ste. Do- - mi- ne,
Chri- ste. Do- -
- su Chri- ste. Do- - mi-
46
-ne, Do- mi- ne De- us, A- gnus De- i, Fi- li-
Do- mi- ne De- us, A- gnus De- - i, Fi-
- mi- ne, Do- mi- ne De- us, A- gnus De- i, Fi- li- us
-ne, Do- mi- ne De- us, Fi- li- us Pa-
51
-us Pa- tris. pec- ca- ta
- li- us Pa- tris.
Pa- tris. Qui tol- - - -
- tris. Qui tol- - - -

56
mun- - di, mi- se- re- re no- bis. Qui tol- lis
mi- - se- re- re no- bis. Qui tol- lis pec-
-lis pec- ca- ta mun- di, mi- se- re- re no- bis. Qui tol- lis pec-
-lis pec- ca- ta mun- di, mi- se- re- re no- bis. Qui tol- lis
4 [♯]3
62
pec- ca- ta mun- - di, su- sci- pe, su- sci-
-ca- ta mun- - di, su- sci- pe, su- sci-
-ca- ta mun- - - di, su- sci- pe, su- sci-
pec- ca- ta mun- di, su- - sci-
6
5 6 [5] 5
3 4 [4] 3
67
-pe de- pre- ca- ti- o- nem no- stram, de- pre- ca- ti-
-pe de- pre- ca- ti-
-pe de- pre- ca- ti- o- nem no- - stram, de- pre- ca- ti-
-pe de- pre- ca- ti- o- nem no- - stram, de- pre- ca- ti-
[6]
♮

73
-o- nem no- stram. Qui se- - - des mi- se-
-o- nem no- stram. ad de- xte- ram Pa- - - tris,
-o- nem no- stram. Qui se- - des mi- se-
-o- nem no- stram. ad de- xte- ram Pa- tris,
4 [♯]3 ♯ 4 3
79
-re- re no- - bis. tu so- lus san- ctus. Tu so- lus
Quo- ni- am tu so- lus san- ctus. Tu
-re- re no- - bis. tu so- lus san- ctus.
Quo- ni- am Tu so- lus Do- mi-
6
84
Do- mi- nus. so- lus Al- tis- si- mus, Je- su Chri-
so- - lus Al- tis- si- mus, Je- - su Chri-
Tu so- - lus Al- tis- si- mus, Je- su Chri- ste.
-nus. so- lus Al- tis- si- mus, Je- su Chri-
♯

89
- ste. Cum San- cto
- ste. Cum Sancto Spi- ri- tu, in glo- - -
Cum San- cto Spi- ri- tu, in glo- - - ri-
-ste. Cum San- cto Spi- ri- tu, in glo-
7 6 7 6 6 6
95
Spi- ri- tu, in glo- ri- a, in glo- ri- a, in glo- -
- ri- a, in glo- - ri- a, in glo- ri- a
-a, in glo- - - ri- a De-
- - ri- a, in glo- ri- a, in glo- ri- a, in glo- ri-
4 [♯]3 4 3
100
- - ri- a A- - -
De- i Pa- - tris. A-
- i Pa- - - tris. A- - men, a-
-a De- - i Pa- - tris. A-
4 3 5 ♯6 7 6 2 7 6

13

Credo

15
- mi- num Je- - sum Chri- stum, Fi- li- um De- i u- ni- ge- ni-
-num Je- sum Chri- stum, Fi- li- um De- i u- - ni- ge- ni-
Je- - sum Chri- stum, Fi- li- um De- i u- - ni- ge- ni-
- mi- num Je- sum Chri- stum, Fi- li- um De- i u- ni- ge- ni-
♯ 5 4 [♯]3
20
-tum. De- um de De-
-tum. Et ex Pa- tre na- tum an- te om- ni- a sae- cu- la.
-tum. Et ex Pa- tre na- tum an- te om- ni- - a sae- cu- la.
-tum. Et ex Pa- tre na- tum an- te om- ni- a sae- cu- la. De- um de
[6] 5 ♯6 4 [♯]3 [6]
26
-o, De- um ve- rum de De- o
lu- men de lu- mi- ne, de De- o ve-
lu- men de lu- mi- ne, De- um ve- rum de
De- o, de De- o ve- ro, de

31
ve- ro.
- ro.
De- o ve- ro. Ge- ni- tum, non fa- ctum, con- sub- stan- ti- a- lem Pa-
De- o ve- ro. Ge- - ni- tum, non fa- ctum, con- sub- stan- ti- a- lem
[6]
36
per quem, per quem om- ni- a
per quem, per quem om- ni-
- - tri: per quem, per quem om- ni-
Pa- - tri: per quem, per quem om- ni- a
4 3
41
fa- cta sunt. Qui pro- pter nos ho- mi- nes, et pro- pter
-a fa- cta sunt. et
-a fa- cta sunt. Qui pro- pter nos ho- - mi- nes, et pro- pter no-
fa- cta sunt. Qui pro- pter nos ho- mi- nes, et pro- pter
7 ♯6

46
no- stram sa- lu- tem de- scèn- dit de cae- -
pro- pter no- stram sa- lu- tem
-stram sa- lu- tem de- scen- dit de cae- -
no- stram sa- lu- tem de- scen- - dit, de- scen- dit de cae-
4 3 4 [♯]3
52
-lis. Et in- - car- na- - tus est de Spi- ri- tu San- cto
Et in- - car- na- tus est de Spi- ri- tu San-
-lis. Et in- - car- na- tus est de Spi- ri- tu San- cto
-lis. Et in- - car- na- - tus est de Spi- ri-
5 ♮ ♯
57
ex Ma- ri- a Vir- gi- ne: et ho- mo fa- ctus est.
-cto ex Ma- ri- a Vir- gi- ne: et ho- mo fa- ctus est.
ex Ma- ri- a Vir- gi- ne: et ho- mo fa- ctus est.
-tu San- cto et ho- mo fa- ctus est.
4 3 ♯ 5

63
Cru- ci- fi- - - - xus e- ti-
Cru- ci- fi- - - - xus e- ti- am
Cru- - ci- fi- - - xus e- ti-
Cru- ci- fi- - - xus
69
-am pro no- - - bis:
pro no- - - - bis:
-am pro no- - - bis: sub Pon- - ti- o Pi-
sub Pon- ti- o Pi-
74
Et re- sur- re- xit
pas- - sus, et se- pul- tus est. Et re- sur- re- xit
-la- to pas- sus, et se- pul- tus est. Et re- sur- re- xit
-la- to pas- sus, et se- pul- tus est. Et re- sur- re- xit

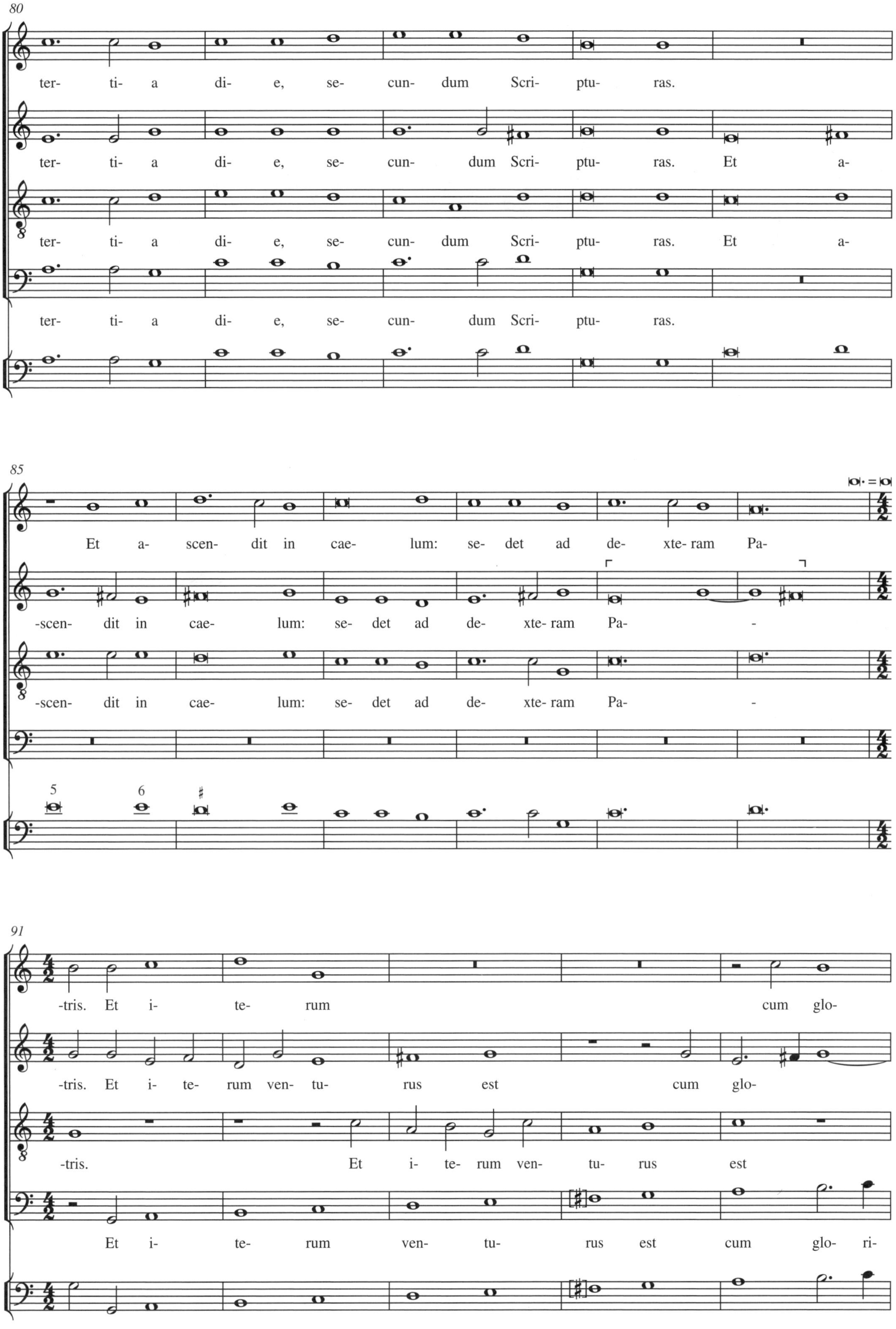
80
ter- ti- a di- e, se- cun- dum Scri- ptu- ras.
ter- ti- a di- e, se- cun- dum Scri- ptu- ras. Et a-
ter- ti- a di- e, se- cun- dum Scri- ptu- ras. Et a-
ter- ti- a di- e, se- cun- dum Scri- ptu- ras.
85
Et a- scen- dit in cae- lum: se- det ad de- xte- ram Pa-
-scen- dit in cae- lum: se- det ad de- xte- ram Pa- -
-scen- dit in cae- lum: se- det ad de- xte- ram Pa- -
5 6 ♯
91
-tris. Et i- te- rum cum glo-
-tris. Et i- te- rum ven- tu- rus est cum glo-
-tris. Et i- te- rum ven- tu- rus est
Et i- te- rum ven- tu- rus est cum glo- ri-

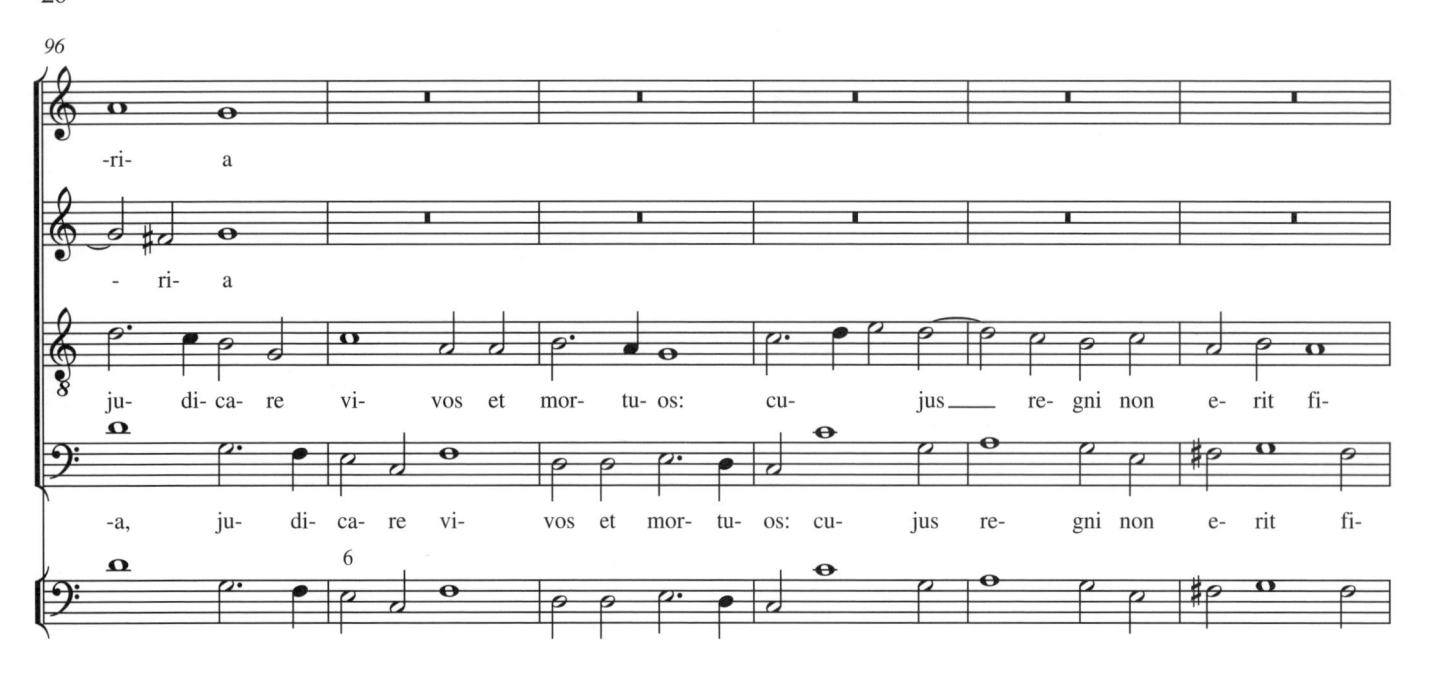

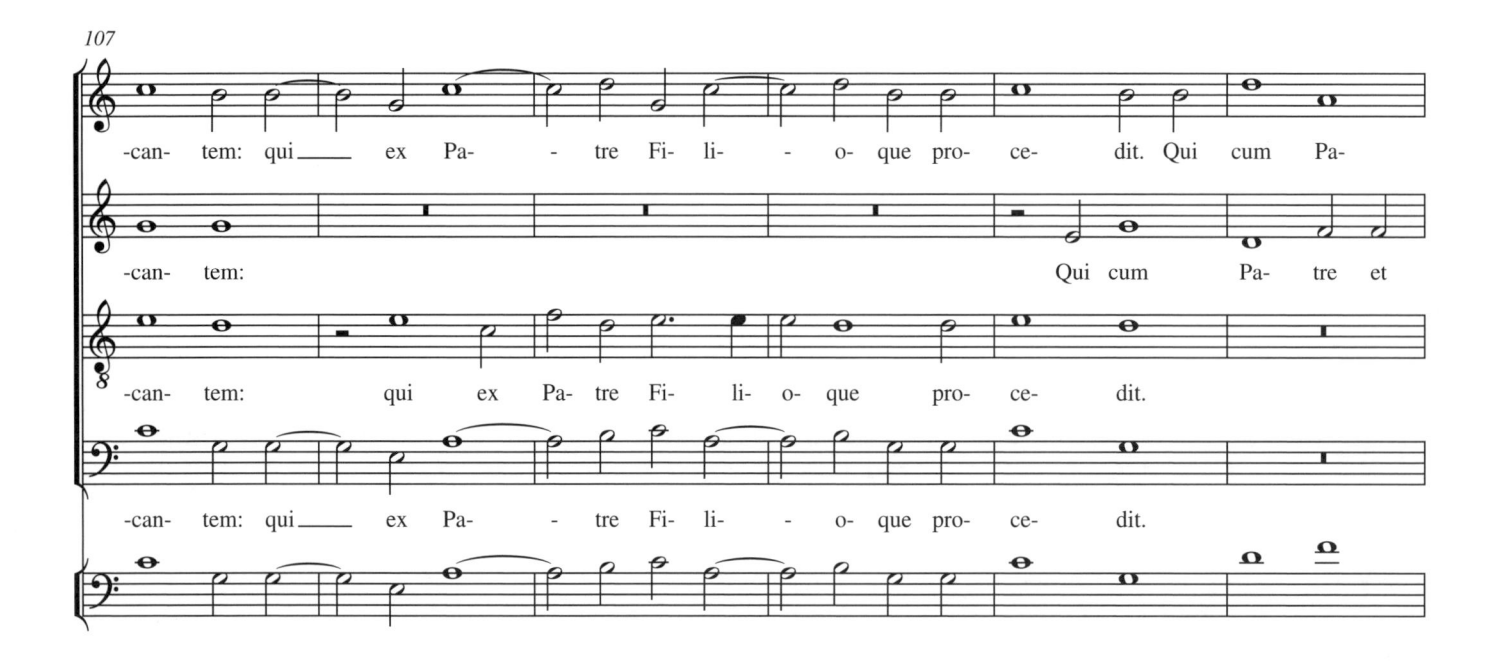

[Sheet music, measures 96–107]

Voice 1 (m. 96): -ri- a

Voice 2 (m. 96): -ri- a

Voice 3 (m. 96): ju- di- ca- re vi- vos et mor- tu- os: cu- jus re- gni non e- rit fi-

Voice 4 (m. 96): -a, ju- di- ca- re vi- vos et mor- tu- os: cu- jus re- gni non e- rit fi-

(m. 102): Et in Spi- ri- tum San- ctum, Do- mi- num, et vi- vi- fi-
Et in Spi- ri- tum San- ctum, Do- mi- num, et vi- vi- fi-
-nis. Et in Spi- ri- tum San- ctum, Do- mi- num, et vi- vi- fi-
-nis. Et in Spi- ri- tum San- ctum, Do- mi- num, et vi- vi- fi-

(m. 107): -can- tem: qui ex Pa- tre Fi- li- o- que pro- ce- dit. Qui cum Pa-
-can- tem: Qui cum Pa- tre et
-can- tem: qui ex Pa- tre Fi- li- o- que pro- ce- dit.
-can- tem: qui ex Pa- tre Fi- li- o- que pro- ce- dit.

113
-tre et Fi- li- o et con- glo- ri- fi- ca-
Fi- li- o et con- glo- ri- fi-
si- mul ad- o- ra- - - tur,
si- mul ad- o- ra- - tur,
6
5 6
♮
118
-tur: Et u- nam
-ca- tur: qui lo- cu- tus est per Pro- phe- - tas. Et
qui lo- cu- - tus est per Pro- phe- tas. Et u- nam san-
qui lo- cu- tus est per Pro- phe- tas. Et u-
4 [♯]3
124
et a- po- sto- li- cam Ec- cle- si-
u- nam et a- po- sto- - li- cam Ec- cle-
-ctam ca- tho- - - li- cam et a- po- sto- li- cam Ec- cle- si-
-nam, et u- nam san- ctam ca- tho- li- cam
5 6 5 6 7 6 7 3

129
-am. Con- fi- - te- or
- si- am. Con- fi- - te- or in
-am. Con- fi- - te- or u- num ba- pti- -
Con- fi- - te- or u- num ba- pti- -
134
u- num ba- pti- - sma in re- mis- si-
re- mis- si- o- nem pec- ca- to- - -
-sma in re- mis- si- o- nem pec- ca-
- sma in re- mis- si- o- nem pec- ca- to-
139
-o- nem pec- ca- to- rum. Et ex- spe- cto re- sur- re- cti-
-rum. Et ex- spe- cto re- sur- re- cti-
-to- - rum. Et ex- spe- cto re- sur- re- cti-
- - rum. Et ex- spe- cto re- sur- re- cti-

23

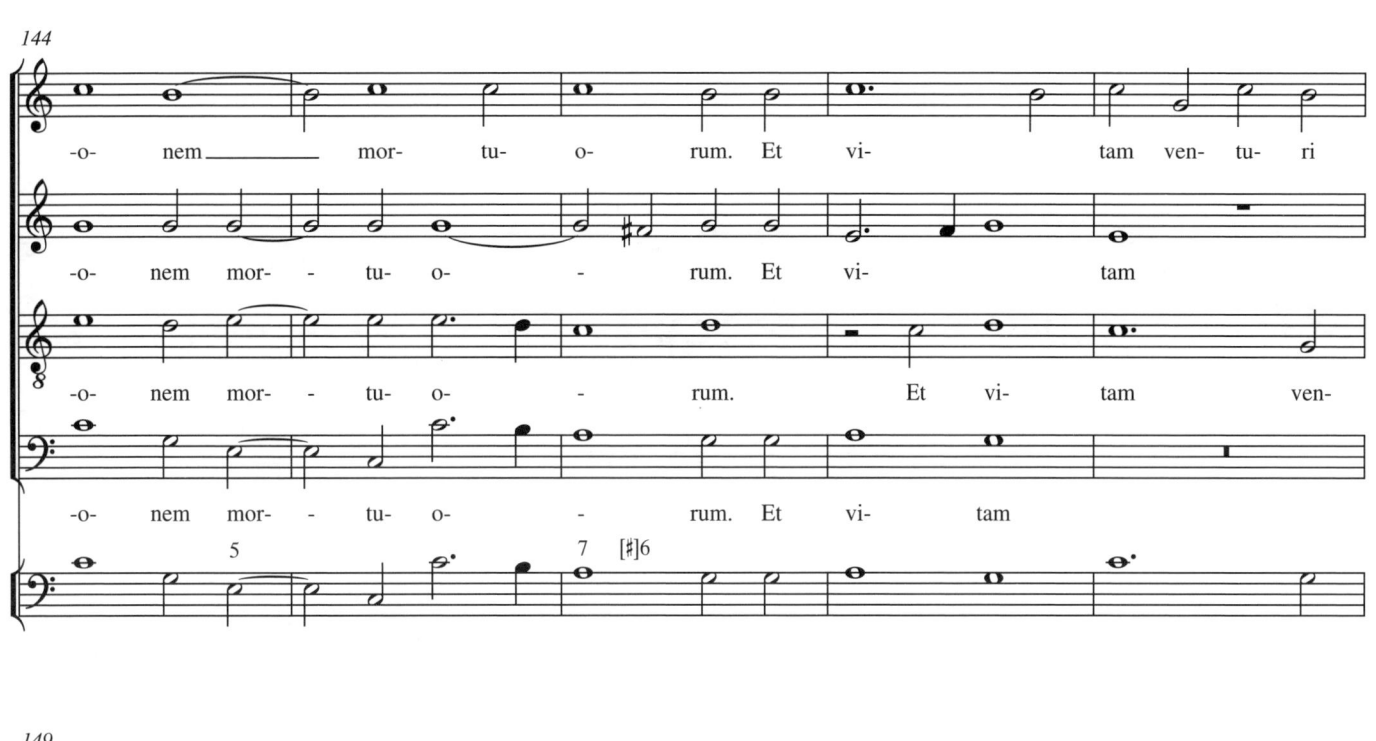

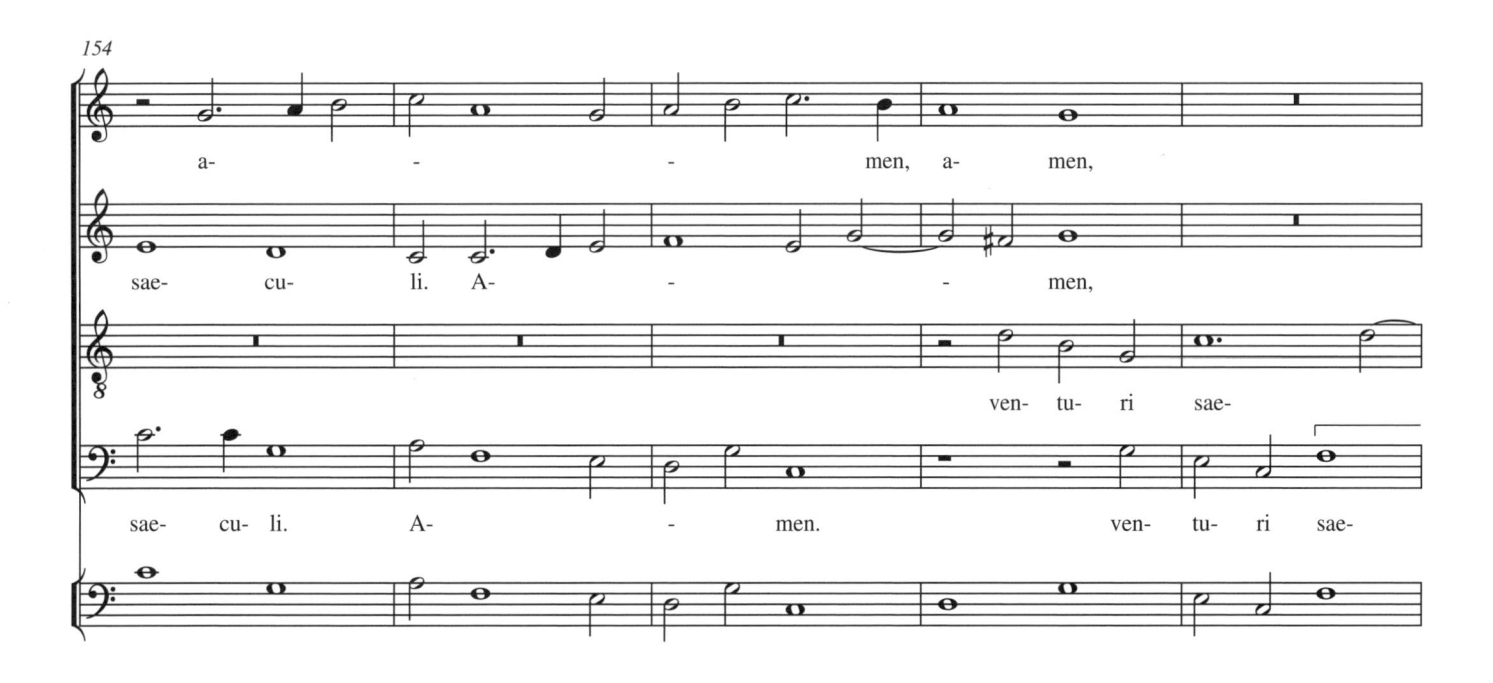

159
a- - - men, a-
a- - - -
- cu- li. A- - - -
- - cu- li.
164
- - - men.
- - - men. ven- tu- ri
- men, a- - - - - men.
A- - - - men. ven-
7 6 4 3
169
ven- tu- ri sae- cu- li. A- men, a- men.
sae- cu- li. A- men, a- men.
ven- tu- ri sae- cu- li. A- men, a- men.
-tu- ri sae- cu- li. A- men, a- - men, a- men.

Sanctus

15
ter- - - - ra glo- ri- a tu-
et ter- - - - ra glo- ri- a
20
Ho- san- - - na in ex-
Ho- san- - na in ex- cel-
- - - a, glo- ri- a tu- - a.
tu- - a. Ho- san- -
25
-cel- - - sis, ho- san- -
- - - sis, ho- san-
Ho- san- - - -
- na, ho- san- - na in ex- cel- -

30
-na, ho- san- - na in ex- cel- -
- na in ex- cel- - - sis,
- - na, ho- san- -
-sis, ho- san- - - na, ho- san-
[♮] 7 6
35
- - - - - sis.
ho- san- - - na in ex- cel- - sis.
- na in ex- cel- - - - [sis.]
- na in ex- cel- - - - sis.
41
Be- - ne- di-
Be- ne- di- -
Be- ne- di- - ctus qui
Be- ne- di- - - ctus

46
- ctus qui ve- - nit
- ctus in no- mi- ne Do- mi- ni, in no- mi- ne Do-
ve- nit in no- mi- ne Do- - mi-
qui ve- - nit
4 [♯]3
7 6 4 [♯]3
51
Ho- san- - - na in ex- cel- -
- mi- ni. Ho- san- - na in ex- cel- -
-ni. Ho- san-
Ho- san- - - na,
♯ [♯] 4 [♯]3
56
- - sis, ho- san- - na,
- - sis, ho- san- - na in ex-
- - - - -
ho- san- - na in ex- cel- - sis, ho- san-
♮ ♯ ♯

Agnus Dei

5
A- gnus De- - - i,
- - - - i, A- - gnus De-
- - i, A- - gnus De-
- - - - i,
5 6 [6] ♮ [6]
10
qui tol- - - -
- - i, qui tol- - -
- - i,
qui tol- - -
5 6 6
15
- lis pec- ca- ta mun- di:
- lis pec- ca- ta mun- - di: mi- - se- re- re
pec- ca- ta mun- - - di: mi- se-
-lis pec- ca- ta mun- - - di: mi- se-

20
mi- se- re- re no- - -
no- bis, mi- se- re- re no- - bis,
-re- re no- - bis, mi- se- re- re no- -
-re- re no- bis, mi- - se- re- re no- -
25
-bis, mi- se- re- re no- - bis.
mi- - se- re- re no- - bis.
-bis, mi- se- re- re no- - bis.
-bis, mi- se- re- re no- - bis.

Messa a cappella seconda
Kyrie

15
-son. Chri- ste e- le- i- son, Chri- ste e- le- i- son,
-son. Chri- ste, Chri- ste e-
-son. Chri- ste, Chri- ste e- le- i- son, Chri- ste e- le- i-
-son.
6
20
e- le- - - i- son, Chri-
-le- i- son, Chri- ste e- le- i- son,
-son, e- le- - - i- son, Chri- - ste e- le- i- son,
Chri- ste e- le- i- son, e- le- i- son, Chri- - ste e- le- i- son, e-
♭
25
-ste, Chri- ste e- le- - i- son,
Chri- ste, Chri- ste e- le- i- son, Chri- - ste e-
Chri- ste, Chri-
-le- i- son, Chri- ste e- le- i- son, Chri- ste,
4 [♮]3 [♮] 7 6

30
Chri- ste, Chri- ste e- le- - i- son.
-le- i- son, Chri- ste e- le- i- son, Chri- ste e- le- i- son.
-ste e- le- i- son, Chri- - ste e- le- i- son.
Chri- ste e- le- i- son, Chri- ste e- le- i- son.
35
Ky- ri- e e- le- i- son,
Ky- ri- e e- le- i- son,
Ky- ri- e e- le- i- son, Ky- ri-
Ky- ri- e e- le- i- son, Ky- ri- e e-
40
Ky- ri- e e- le- i- son, Ky- ri- e e- le- i-
Ky- ri- e e- le- i- son, Ky- ri- e e- le- i-
-e e- le- i- son, Ky- ri- e e- - le- i-
-le- i- son, e- le- i- son, Ky- ri- e e- le- i-

Gloria

-ta- tis. Lau- da- mus te. Ad- o- ra- mus te. Glo-
-ta- tis. Lau- da- mus te. Ad- - o- ra- mus
- ta- tis. Lau- da- mus te. Be- ne- di- ci- mus te.
-ta- tis. Lau- da- mus te. Be- ne- di- ci- mus te. Glo-
-ri- fi- ca- - mus te. Gra- - ti- as a- gi- mus ti-
te. Glo- ri- fi- ca- mus te. Gra- ti- as a- gi- mus ti-
Glo- ri- fi- ca- mus te. Gra- ti- as a- gi- mus ti-
-ri- fi- ca- mus te. Gra- - ti- as a- gi- mus ti- bi
- bi pro- - pter ma- gnam glo- ri- am, glo-
- bi pro- pter ma- gnam glo- ri- am,
- bi pro- - pter ma- gnam glo- ri- am,
pro- pter ma- gnam glo- ri- am, glo-

20
- - - ri- am, glo- ri- am tu-
glo- - - - ri- am, glo- ri- am
glo- ri- am tu-
- - - ri- am
25
- - am.
tu- - - am.
- - am. Do- mi- ne De- us, Rex cae- - le-
Do- mi- ne De- us, Rex cae- le-
6 6 6 6 7 6
30
De- us Pa- ter om- ni- po- tens.
De- us Pa- - ter om- ni- po- tens. Do- mi- ne Fi-
-stis, De- us Pa- ter om- ni- po- tens.
-stis, Do- mi- ne Fi-
7 6 4 3 6 6 4 3

35
Do- mi- ne Fi- li Je- su Chri- ste. Do- mi- ne
-li u- ni- ge- ni- te Je- - su Chri- ste.
Do- mi- ne Fi- li Je- su Chri- ste.
-li u- ni- ge- ni- te Do- mi- ne
41
De- us, A- gnus De- i,
Fi- li- us Pa- - -
Do- mi- ne De- us, A- gnus De- i, Fi- li- us Pa-
De- us, A- gnus De- i, Fi- li- us Pa- -
46
Qui tol- - lis pec- ca- ta
- tris. Qui tol- - lis pec- ca-
- tris. Qui tol- - lis pec- ca- ta mun-
- tris. Qui tol- - lis pec- ca- ta

51
mun- di, mi- se-
- ta mun- di, mi- se- re- re no- - bis, mi- se-
- - di, mi- - se- re- re no- bis,
mun- - di, mi- - se- re- re no- bis, mi- se-
56
-re- re no- bis.
Qui tol- lis pec- ca- ta mun-
-re- - re no- bis. Qui tol- - lis pec- ca- ta mun-
mi- se- re- re no- bis. Qui tol- lis pec-
-re- re no- bis.
61
- di,
- - di, su- - sci- pe de- - pre- ca- ti- o- nem no-
-ca- ta mun- - di,
su- sci- pe de- pre- ca- ti- o- nem no-

66
Qui se- - des ad de- - xte- ram Pa-
- stram. Qui se- - - des
Qui se- - des ad
- stram. Qui se- - des ad de- xte-
4 3
6
71
- - tris,
mi- - se- re- re no- -
de- xte- ram Pa- tris, mi- se- re- re no- -
-ram Pa- - tris,
4 [♮]3 [6]
76
Quo- ni- am tu so- lus san- ctus. Tu so- - lus
-bis. Quo- ni- am tu so- lus san- ctus. Tu so-
-bis. Quo- ni- am Tu so- lus Do- mi- nus. Tu so-
Quo- ni- am Tu so- lus Do- mi- nus. Tu
6

81
Al- tis- - si- mus, Je- su Chri- ste.
- lus Al- tis- si- mus, Je- su Chri- ste.
- lus Al- tis- si- mus, Je- - su Chri- ste. Cum San- cto Spi-
so- lus Al- tis- si- mus, Je- su Chri- ste. Cum San- cto
87
in glo- ri- a De- i Pa- tris. A- -
in glo- ri- a De- i Pa- - tris. A- men.
- ri- tu, in glo- ri- a De- i Pa-
Spi- ri- tu, in glo- ri- a De-
92
-men, a- men, a- men. in glo-
in glo- - - -
- tris. A- men, a- men. in glo- - - ri-
-i Pa- tris. A- men. in glo-

97
- - ri- a, in glo- ri- a De- i Pa-
- - ri- a, in glo- ri- a De- i Pa-
-a, in glo- ri- a, in glo- ri- a De- i Pa-
- - ri- a, in glo- ri- a De- i Pa-
4 [♮]3 6
102
- tris. A- - - men. in glo- ri-
-tris. A- - - men. in glo- ri- a
-tris. A- - - - men. in glo- ri- a
-tris. A- - - - men. in glo- ri-
5 6 5 6 5 6
108
-a De- i Pa- tris. A- - - men.
De- i Pa- - - tris. A- men.
De- i Pa- - - tris. A- men.
-a De- i Pa- - - tris. A- men.
7 3 6 4 [5 4] 5 3

Credo

16
Chri- stum, u- - ni- ge-
Chri- stum, Fi- li- um De- - i u- ni-
- sum Chri- stum, Fi- li- um De- - i u- - ni- ge-
Chri- stum, Fi- li- um De- - i u- - ni- ge-
7 6 [5] 5
[♮]3 4 [4] [♮]3
21
- ni- tum. Et ex Pa- tre na- tum an- te
-ge- ni- tum. Et ex Pa- tre na- - tum an- te
- ni- tum. Et ex Pa- tre na- - - tum an- te
- ni- tum. Et ex Pa- tre na- tum, et ex Pa- tre na- tum an- te
4 3
7 6 [6]
♭
27
om- ni- a sae- - cu- la.
om- ni- a sae- - cu- la.
om- ni- a sae- - cu- la. De- um de De- o, lu- men de lu- mi- ne,
om- ni- a sae- - cu- la. De- um de De- o, lu- men de lu- mi-
6

32
Ge- ni- tum, non
Ge- ni-
De- um ve- rum de De- - o ve- ro.
-ne, De- - um ve- rum de De- - o ve- ro.
37
fa- - - ctum,
-tum, non fa- - - ctum, con- - sub- stan- ti- a- lem Pa-
con- sub- stan- - ti- a- lem Pa-
con- sub- stan- ti- a- lem Pa-
42
per quem om- ni- a fa- cta sunt. et pro- pter no-
-tri: Qui pro- pter nos ho- mi- nes,
-tri: per quem om- ni- a fa- cta sunt. Qui pro- pter nos ho- mi-
-tri: per quem om- ni- a fa- cta sunt. et pro- pter no-

47
- stram sa- lu- tem de- scen- dit de cae- - lis. Et
de- scen- dit de cae- - - lis. Et
-nes, de- scen- dit de cae- - - lis. Et
-stram sa- lu- tem de- scen- dit de cae- - lis. Et
4 [♯]3 4 [♯]3 ♮
52
in- car- na- - tus est de Spi- ri- tu San- - cto ex
in- car- na- tus est de Spi- ri- tu San- cto ex
in- car- na- tus est de Spi- ri- tu San- cto ex
in- car- na- tus est de Spi- ri- tu San- cto ex
4 [♯]3 7 6 4 [♯]3 ♮
57
Ma- ri- a Vir- gi- ne: et ho- mo fa- ctus
Ma- ri- a Vir- gi- ne: et ho- - mo fa- ctus
Ma- ri- a Vir- gi- ne: et ho- mo fa- - ctus
Ma- ri- a Vir- gi- ne: et ho- mo fa- ctus
7 6 ♯ ♮

47

48

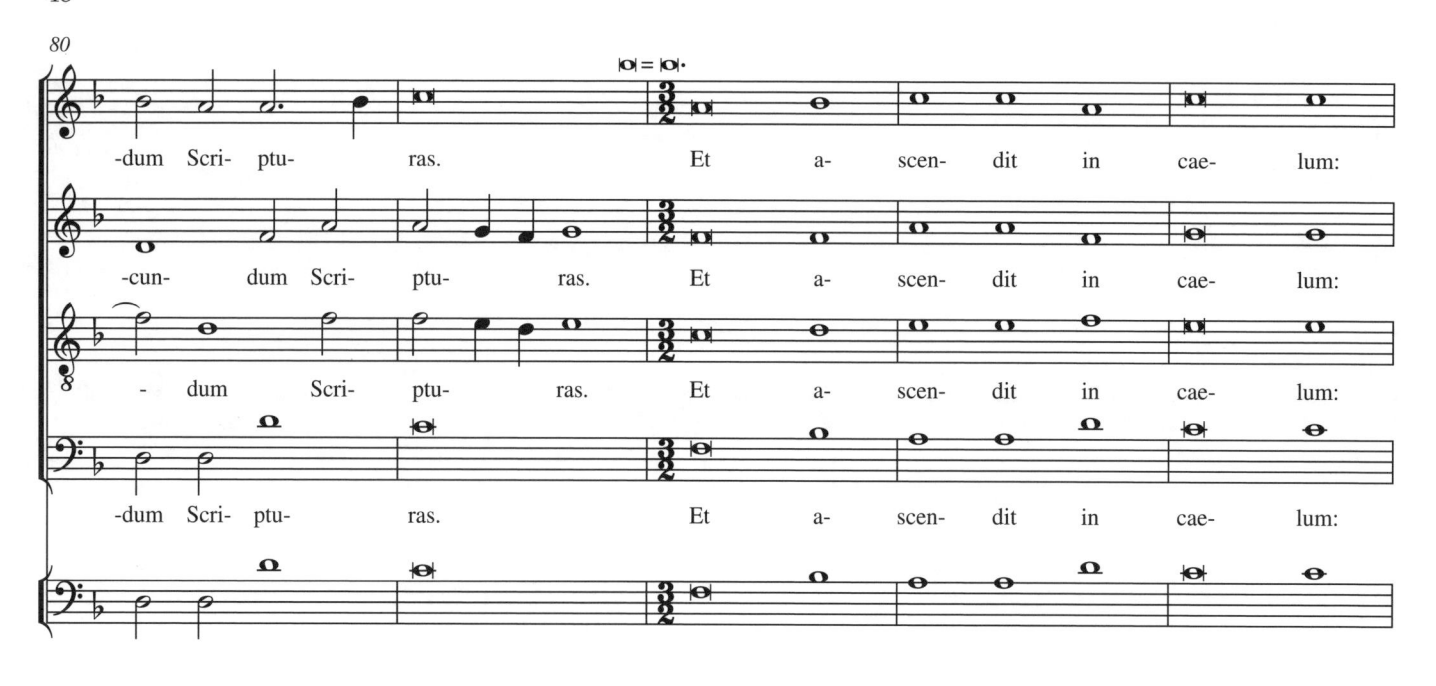

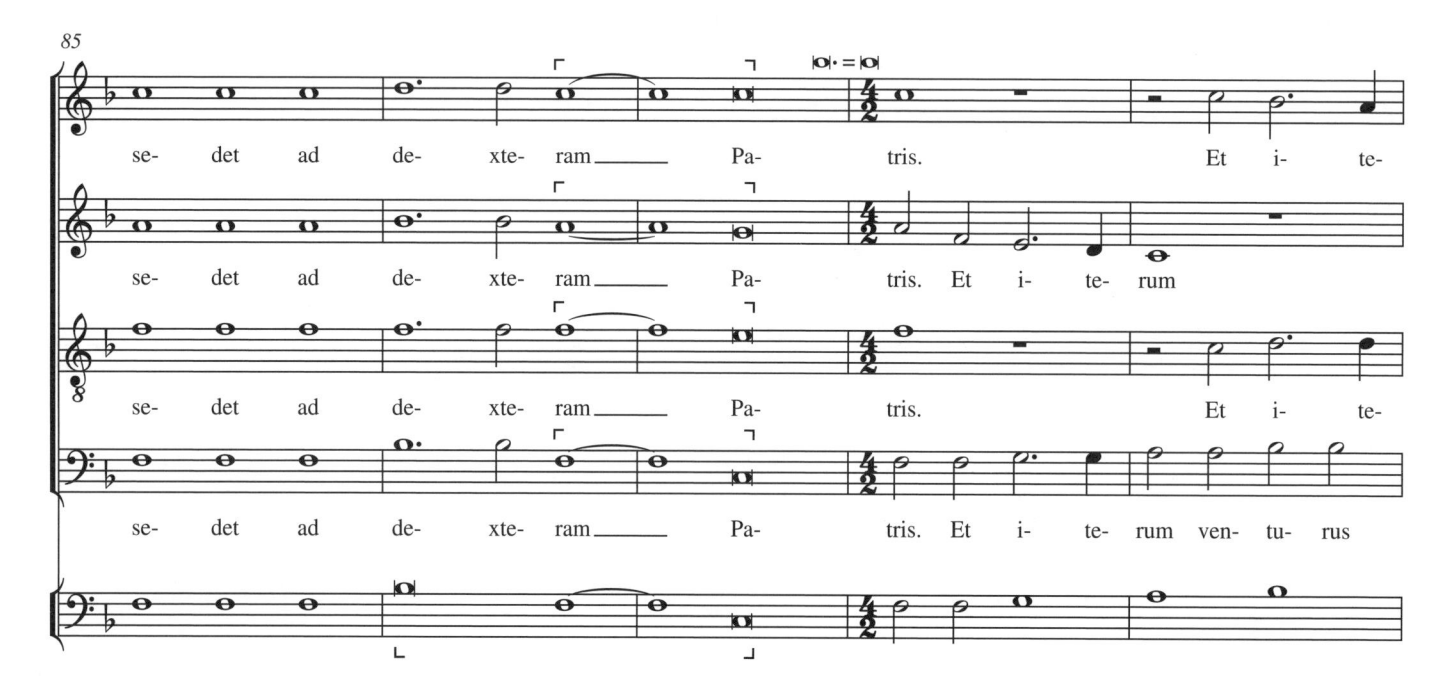

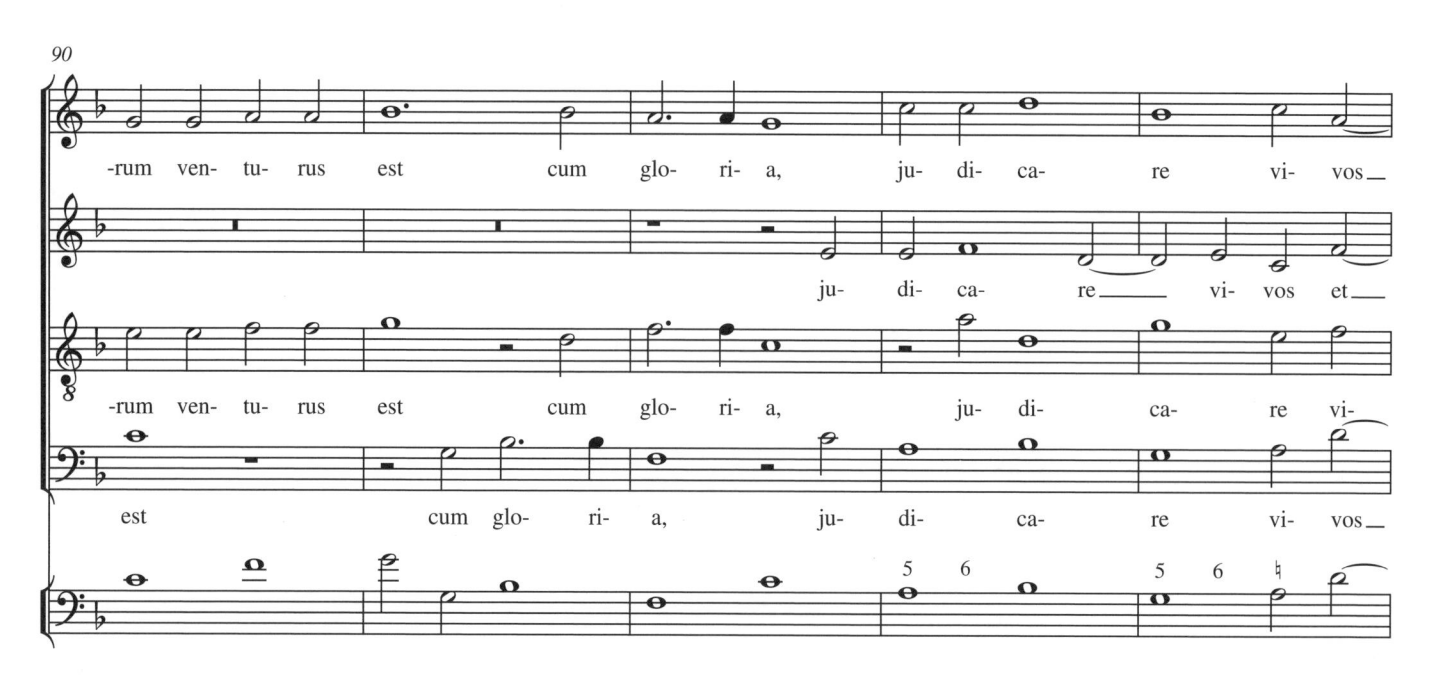

49

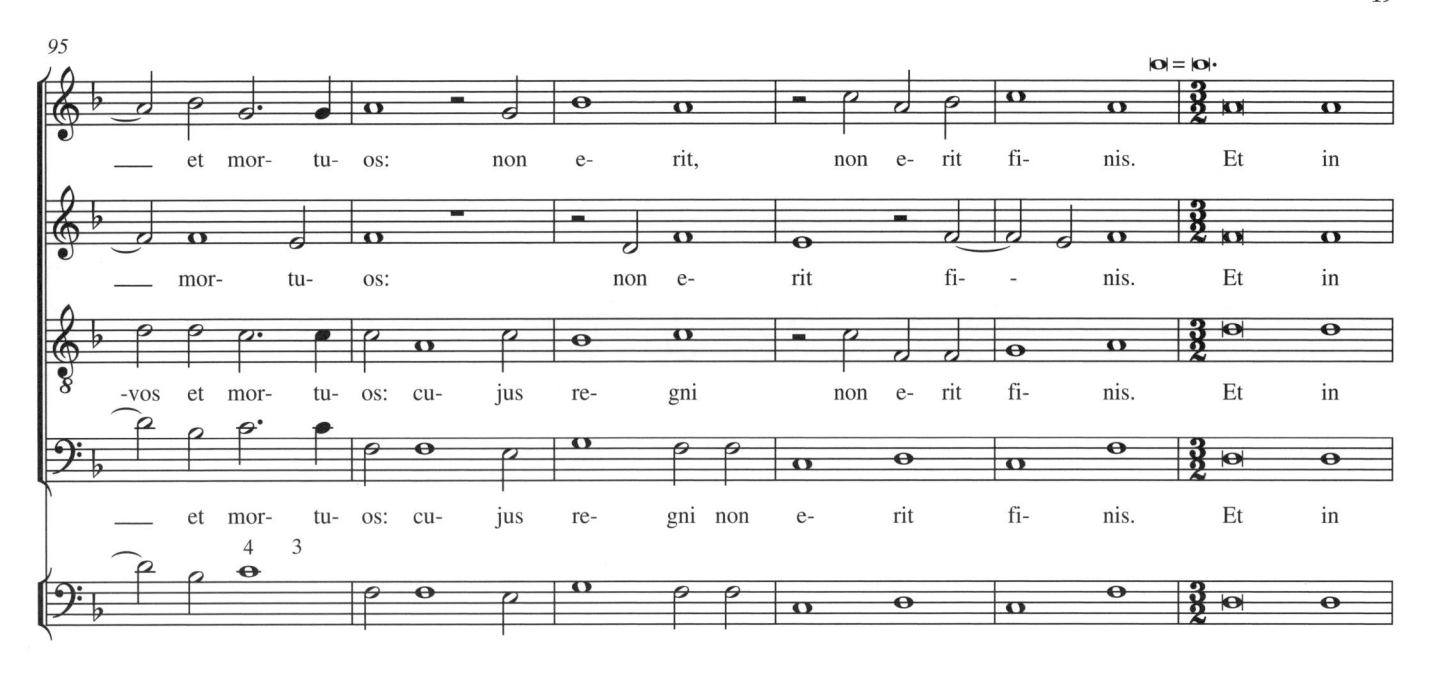

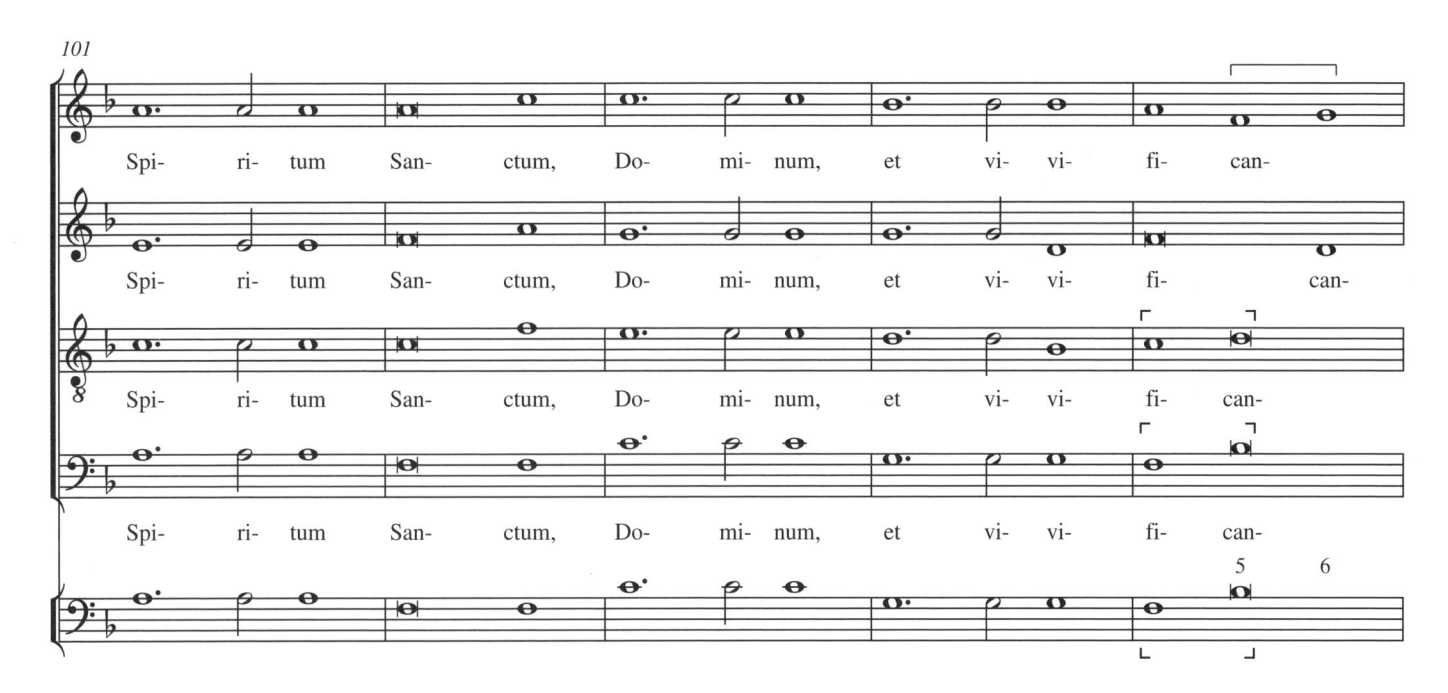

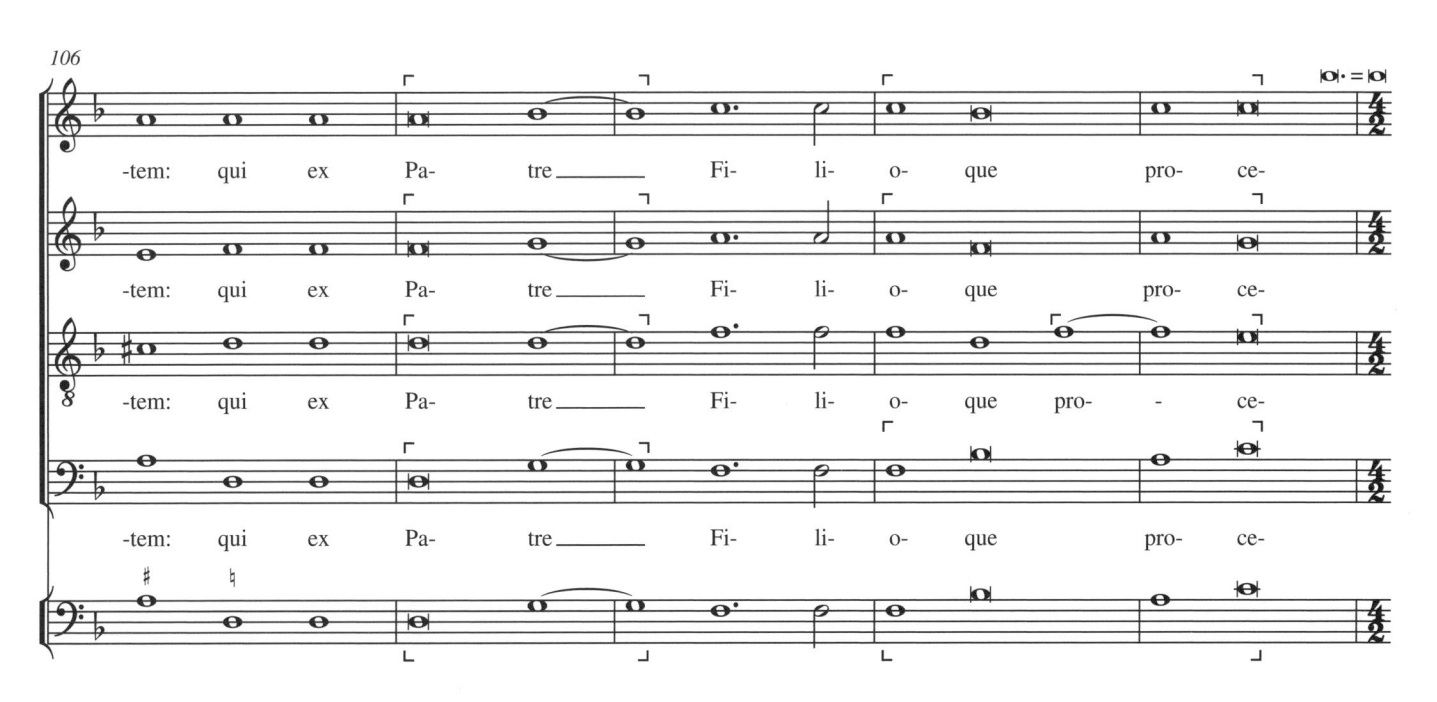

111
-dit. si- - mul ad- o-
-dit. Qui cum Pa- tre et Fi- li- o si- mul ad- o- ra-
-dit. Qui cum Pa- tre et Fi- li- o si- mul ad- o- ra-
-dit. Qui cum Pa- tre et Fi- li- o si- mul ad- o- ra-
116
-ra- tur, et con- glo- ri- fi- ca- tur: qui lo- cu- tus est per Pro-
-tur, et con- glo- ri- fi- ca- tur: qui lo- - cu- tus
-tur, et con- glo- ri- fi- - ca- tur: qui lo- cu- tus est
-tur, et con- glo- ri- fi- ca- tur:
7 6 4 3
121
-phe- - tas.
est per Pro- phe- tas. Et u- - nam san- ctam ca- tho- li-
per Pro- phe- tas. Et u- - nam,
per Pro- phe- tas. Et u- - nam san- ctam ca- tho- li-
4 3 4 3 6

126
Et u- - nam san- ctam ca- tho- li- cam et a- po-
-cam, et u- - nam et a- po- sto- li- cam
et u- - nam san- ctam ca- tho- li- cam et a- po-
-cam et a- po- sto- li- cam
131
-sto- li- cam Ec- cle- si- am. Con- fi- te- or u- num ba- pti-
Ec- cle- - si- am. Con- fi- te- or u- num ba- pti- sma
-sto- li- cam Ec- cle- si- am. u- num ba- pti- sma, u-
Ec- cle- si- am. Con- fi- te- or u- num ba- pti- sma, u-
4 [♮]3 4 [♮]3
136
- - sma
in re- mis- si- o- - nem pec- ca- to-
- num ba- - pti- sma in re- mis- si- o- nem pec- ca- to-
-num ba- pti- sma in re- mis- si- o- nem pec- ca-
9 8 4 [♮]3 6 5 6

141
Et ex- spe- -
- - rum.
- - rum. Et ex- spe- -
-to- - rum. Et ex- spe-
7 4 3
145
- cto re- sur- re- cti- o- nem mor- tu-
Et ex- spe- cto re- - sur- re- - cti- o- nem mor-
-cto, ex- spe- - cto re- sur- re- cti- o- - nem mor-
- - cto re- sur- re- cti- o- - nem mor-
6 4 3
150
-o- rum. Et vi- tam ven- tu- ri sae-
- tu- o- rum. Et vi- tam ven-
- tu- o- rum. ven- tu- ri sae- cu- li, et vi-
- tu- o- rum. ven- tu- ri sae- cu- li, ven-
4 3 6

155
- cu- li, et vi- tam ven- tu- ri sae- cu- li. A- men,
-tu- ri sae- cu- li, ven- tu- ri sae- cu- li. A- men, a-
-tam ven- tu- ri sae- cu- li, ⟨ven- tu- ri sae- cu- li.⟩ A-
-tu- ri sae- - cu- li. A- -
4 [♮]3
160
a- - - men,
- - - men, a- men,
- men, a- - men, a- men, a- -
- - - - men, a- -
7 6 5 4 [♮]3 7 6
165
a- - - men, a- men.
a- - - men, a- men, a- men.
- - - - men, a- men.
- - - - men, a- men.
4 3

Sanctus

30
hosanna in excel- - -
in ex- cel- - - - -
- - - - -
- - sis, ho- san- na in ex- cel- -
4 3
35
-sis. Be- ne- di- - ctus
-sis. Be- ne- di- ctus qui ve-
-sis. Be- ne- di- - ctus qui ve-
-sis. Be- ne- di- ctus qui ve-
6
40
in no- - - mi- ne
- nit in no-
- nit in no- - mi-
- nit in no-
7 6 4 3

44
Do- - mi- ni, in no- mi- ne Do- mi- ni,
- mi- ne Do- mi- ni, in no- mi- ne Do- mi- ni, in no- mi-
-ne Do- - mi- ni, in no- mi- ne Do- mi- ni, in no- mi-
- - mi- ne, in no- mi- ne Do- mi- ni,
49
in no- mi- ne Do- - mi- ni.
-ne Do- - - mi- - ni.
-ne Do- - - - mi- ni. Ho- san- na
in no- mi- ne Do- - mi- ni. Ho-
54
Ho- san- na in ex-
Ho- san- na in ex- cel- -
in ex- cel- - - - -
-san- na in ex- cel- - - sis, in ex-

Agnus Dei

6
mi- - se- re- re no- bis, mi- - se- re- re
-lis pec- ca- ta mun- di: mi- se- re- re no- - bis, mi- se-
tol- lis pec- ca- ta mun- di: mi- se- re- re no- - bis, mi- se- re- re
mi- se- re- re no- - bis, mi- se-
4 3 4 3 4 [3]
12
no- - bis, mi- - se- re- - re no- - bis,
-re- re no- bis, mi- se- re- re no- -
no- - - bis, mi- se- re- re no-
-re- re no- - bis, mi- se- re- - re no- - - bis,
18
mi- se- re- re no- - bis.
-bis, mi- se- re- re no- - bis.
-bis, mi- se- re- re no- - - bis.
mi- se- re- re no- - - bis.
6

Messa a cappella terza

Kyrie

15
-son, Ky- - ri- e e- le- i- son. Chri- ste, Chri- - ste e-
-son, Ky- - ri- e e- le- i- son. Chri- ste e-
-son, Ky- ri- e e- le- - i- son. Chri- ste, Chri- ste e-
Ky- ri- e e- le- - i- son. Chri- ste, Chri- ste, Chri- ste, Chri- ste e-
6 ♯
21
- le- i- son, Chri- ste e- le- - i- son,
-le- - i- son, Chri- ste e- le- i-
-le- i- son, Chri- ste e- le- i- son, Chri- ste e- le- i- son, e-
-le- i- son, Chri- ste e- le- i- son,
4 3 [6] 4 3
26
Chri- ste e- le- i- son, e- le- i- son.
-son, Chri- ste e- le- - i- son, e- le- i- son.
-le- - i- son, e- le- i- son, e- le- i- son.
Chri- ste e- le- - i- son, e- le- i- son.
6 ♯ 5 ♯6

31
Ky- ri- e e- - le- i- son, e- le- - i- son, e- le- i- son,
Ky- ri- e e- le- i- son, e- le- i- son,
Ky- ri- e e-
Ky- ri- e e- le- i- son, e- le- - i- son, e- le- i- son, Ky- ri- e e-
Ky- ri- e e- le- i- son, Ky- - ri- e,
37
Ky- ri- e e- le- i- son,
-le- i- son, Ky- - ri- e e- le- i- son, Ky-
-le- i- son, Ky- - ri- e e- le- i- son, Ky- ri-
Ky- ri- e e- le- i- son, Ky- ri- e e- le- i- son,
42
Ky- - ri- e, Ky- ri- e e- le- i- son.
- ri- e e- le- i- son, Ky- ri- e e- le- i- son.
-e e- le- - i- son, Ky- ri- e e- le- i- son.
Ky- ri- e e- le- i- son, e- le- i- son, Ky- ri- e e- le- i- son.

Gloria

16
pro- - pter ma- gnam glo- ri- am, glo- - ri-
- bi pro- - pter ma- gnam glo- ri- am, pro- pter ma- gnam glo- ri-
ti- bi pro- - pter ma- gnam glo- ri- am, pro- pter ma- gnam
ti- bi pro- - pter ma- gnam glo- ri- am tu- am, glo-
21
-am, glo- - ri- am tu- am.
-am, pro- pter ma- gnam glo- ri- am tu- am.
glo- ri- am, glo- ri- am tu- am. Do- mi- ne De- us, Rex cae-
- - ri- am Do- mi- ne De- us, Rex cae-
4 [♯]3
26
De- - us Pa-
-le- - - stis, De- - us Pa- ter om- ni- po-
-le- - - stis, De- - us Pa- - ter om-
[6] ♯ 4 3

31
Do- - mi- ne Fi- li
- ter, Pa- - ter om- ni- po- tens. u- ni- ge- ni- te Je-
-tens, Pa- ter om- ni- po- tens. u- ni- ge- ni- te Je-
-ni- po- tens. Do- mi- ne Fi- li Je-
36
Je- su Chri- ste. Fi- li- us
- su Chri- - ste.
- su Chri- ste. Do- mi- ne De- us, A- gnus De- i, Fi-
- su Chri- ste. Do- mi- ne De- us, A- gnus De- i, Fi-
41
Pa- - - tris. Qui tol- lis, qui
Qui tol- lis, qui tol-
-li- us Pa- - - tris. Qui tol- lis, qui tol-
-li- us Pa- - - tris. Qui tol- lis,

46
tol- - lis mi- - se- re-
- - lis pec- ca- ta mun- di, mi- se-
-lis pec- ca- ta mun- - di, mi- se-
qui tol- lis pec- ca- ta mun- - di, mi- se- re- re
51
- re no- bis, mi- se- re- re no- bis. pec- ca- ta mun-
-re- re no- bis, mi- se- re- re no- bis. pec- ca- ta mun-
-re- re no- bis, mi- se- re- re no- bis. Qui tol- lis pec- ca- ta
no- bis, mi- se- re- re no- bis. Qui tol- lis pec- ca- ta
57
-di, su- - sci- pe
- di, su- - sci- pe de- pre- ca- ti- o- nem no-
mun- di, su- - sci- pe de- pre- ca- - ti- o- nem no-
mun- di, su- sci- pe de- pre- ca- ti- o- nem no-

62
de- pre- ca- ti- o- nem no- stram.
- - stram. Qui
- stram, de- pre- ca- ti- o- nem no- - stram.
- - stram. Qui
9 8 4 [♯3]
67
Qui se- - des ad de- xte- ram Pa-
se- - des mi-
Qui se- - des ad de- xte- ram Pa- - tris,
se- - des ad de- xte- ram Pa- tris
5 6 5
72
-tris, mi- se- re- re no- bis. Tu so-
- se- re- re no- bis. tu so- lus san- ctus. Tu so- lus
mi- se- re- re no- bis. Quo- ni- am tu so- lus san- ctus.
Quo- ni- am
4 [♯]3 [6] 4 3

77
-lus Do- mi- nus. Je- su
Do- mi- nus. Tu so- lus Al- tis- si- mus, Je- - su, Je-
Tu so- lus Al- tis- si- mus, Je- - su, Je-
Tu so- lus Al- tis- si- mus, Je- - su, Je-
5 [♯]6
82
Chri- ste. Cum San- cto Spi- ri- tu, De-
-su Chri- ste. Cum San- cto Spi- ri- tu, De-
-su Chri- ste. Cum San- cto Spi- ri- tu, in glo- ri-
-su Chri- ste. in glo- ri- a
87
-i Pa- tris. A- men. De- i Pa- tris. A- - men, a- men.
-i Pa- tris. A- men. De- - i Pa- tris. A- men.
-a De- - i Pa- - tris. A- men.
De- i Pa- tris. A- men. De- i Pa- - tris. A- men.
[6] ♯ 6

Credo

15
Fi- li- um De- i u- ni- ge- ni- tum.
Et ex Pa- tre
De- i u- ni- ge- - - ni- tum. Et ex
-li- um De- - i u- ni- ge- - ni- tum. Et ex
♮ 7 7 [♯]6
20
De- um de De-
na- tum an- te om- ni- a sae- - cu- la. lu- men de
Pa- tre na- tum an- te om- ni- a sae- cu- la. lu- men de
Pa- tre na- tum De- um de De- o,
[6] 7 [♯]6 5 6 [♯]3 4
25
- o, De- um ve- rum Ge- ni- tum, non fa-
lu- mi- ne, de De- o ve- ro. Ge- ni- tum, non fa-
lu- mi- ne, de De- o ve- ro. Ge- ni- tum, non fa-
De- um ve- rum Ge- ni- tum, non fa-
[5 4] 5 [♯]3 ♯ 5 [♯]3 6 4 [5 4] 5 [♯]3 6

30
-ctum, con- sub- stan- ti- a- lem Pa- tri: per quem om- - ni- a fa- cta
-ctum, con- sub- stan- ti- a- lem Pa- tri: per quem om- - ni- a fa- cta
-ctum, con- sub- stan- ti- a- lem Pa- tri: per quem om- - ni- a fa- cta
-ctum, con- sub- stan- ti- a- lem Pa- tri: per quem om- - ni- a fa- cta
35
sunt, per quem om- ni- a fa- cta sunt. Qui pro- pter nos
sunt, per quem om- ni- a fa- cta sunt.
sunt, per quem om- ni- a fa- cta sunt. Qui pro- pter nos ho-
sunt, per quem om- ni- a fa- cta sunt. Qui pro- pter nos
40
ho- mi- nes, et pro- pter no- stram sa- lu- - tem
et pro- pter no- stram sa- - lu- tem
- mi- nes, et pro- pter no- stram sa- lu- tem de-
ho- mi- nes, et pro- pter no- stram sa- lu- tem de-

Et in- car- na- - tus est
Et in- car- na- tus est de Spi- ri- tu San-
-scen- dit de cae- lis. Et in- car- na- tus est de Spi- ri- tu
-scen- dit de cae- - lis. de Spi- ri- tu
ex Ma- ri- a Vir- gi- ne: et ho- mo, et ho- mo
- cto ex Ma- ri- a Vir- gi- ne: et ho- mo fa-
San- cto ex Ma- ri- a Vir- gi- ne: et ho- mo fa-
San- cto
fa- ctus est. Cru- - ci- fi- - xus e- ti- am pro no-
- ctus est. Cru- - ci- fi- - xus e- ti- am pro no- -
- ctus est. Cru- - ci- fi- xus e- ti- am pro no-
Cru- - ci- fi- xus e- ti- am pro no- -

61
- bis: sub Pon- ti- o Pi- la- to pas- sus,
- bis: pas- - sus, et
- bis: pas- - sus,
-bis: sub Pon- ti- o Pi- la- to pas- sus, et
67
et se- pul- - tus est. Et re- sur- re- xit ter- ti- a di- e, se-
se- pul- tus est. Et re- sur- re- xit ter- ti- a di- e, se-
et se- pul- - tus est. Et re- sur- re- xit ter- ti- a di- e, se-
se- pul- - tus est.
73
-cun- dum Scri- ptu- ras.
-cun- dum Scri- ptu- ras. Et a- scen- dit in cae- -
-cun- dum Scri- ptu- ras. Et a- scen- - dit in cae-
Et a- scen- dit in cae- -

78
se- det ad de- xte- - ram Pa- - tris. ven-
-lum Et i- te- rum
- lum: se- det ad de- xte- ram Pa- - tris. Et i- te- rum ven-
- lum: se- det ad de- xte- ram Pa- -
4 [♯]3 [6] [♯] 7 [♯] 4 3 4 3
83
-tu- rus est, ⟨ven- tu- rus⟩ est cum glo- ri- a, ju- di-
ven- tu- rus est ju- di-
-tu- rus est cum glo- ri- a, ven- tu- rus est cum glo- ri- a, ju- di-
-tris. ven- tu- rus est ju- di-
4 [♯]3 [♯] 4 [♯]3 5
88
-ca- re vi- vos et mor- tu- os: non e-
-ca- re vi- vos et mor- tu- os: cu- - jus re- - gni non
-ca- re vi- vos et mor- tu- os: cu- jus re- gni non
-ca- re vi- vos et mor- tu- os: cu- jus re- gni non e-
5 6 4 [♯]3 ♯ 7 3 4 [♯]3

93
-rit, non e- rit fi- nis, non e- rit fi- nis. Et
e- rit fi- nis, non e- rit, non, non e- rit fi- nis. Et
e- rit, non e- rit fi- nis, non e- - rit fi- nis. Et
-rit, non e- - rit fi- nis, non e- rit fi- nis. Et
4 [♯]3 5 5 [♯]3 6 4 [5] [4] 5 [♯]3
99
in Spi- ri- tum San- ctum, Do- mi- num, et vi- vi- fi- - can- tem:
in Spi- ri- tum San- ctum, Do- mi- num,
in Spi- ri- tum San- ctum, Do- mi- num, et vi- vi- fi- can-
in Spi- ri- tum San- ctum, Do- mi- num, et vi- vi- fi- can-
104
qui ex Pa- - tre Fi- - li- o- que pro-
qui ex Pa- - tre Fi- li- o- que pro-
- tem: qui ex Pa- tre Fi- - li- o- que pro- ce-
- tem: qui ex Pa- - tre Fi- - li- o- que pro- ce-

109
- ce- dit. Qui cum Pa- tre et Fi- li- o
-ce- dit. si- mul
- dit. Qui cum Pa- tre et Fi- li- o
- dit. Qui cum Pa- tre et Fi- li- o
4 3 [6] 5 6 4 3
114
et con- glo- ri- fi- ca- tur: qui lo-
ad- o- ra- tur
si- mul ad- o- ra- tur, et con- glo- ri- fi- ca- tur: qui lo-
si- mul ad- o- ra- tur, et con- glo- ri- fi- ca- - tur:
4 3
119
-cu- tus est per Pro- phe- tas. san- ctam ca- tho- li-
Et u- nam san- ctam ca- tho- li-
-cu- tus est per Pro- phe- tas. Et u- nam san- ctam ca- tho- li- cam
per Pro- phe- tas. san- ctam ca- tho- li- cam et
4 [♯]3 6

124
-cam Con- fi- te- or u-
-cam et a- po- sto- li- cam Ec- cle- si- am. u-
et a- po- sto- li- cam Ec- cle- si- am. Con- fi- te- or
a- po- sto- li- cam Ec- cle- si- am. Con- fi- - te- or
4 [♯]3
129
- num ba- pti- sma Et
-num ba- pti- - sma
in re- mis- si- o- nem pec- ca- - to- rum.
in re- mis- si- o- nem pec- ca- to- - rum.
5 4 3 4 [♯]3 [6] 7 6 4 3 4 [♯]3
134
ex- spe- - cto re- sur- re- cti- o- nem mor-
Et ex- spe- cto re- sur- re- cti- o- nem mor- tu- o-
Et ex- spe- cto re- sur- re- cti- o- nem mor- tu- o-
Et ex- spe- cto re- sur- re- cti- o- nem mor- tu-
♮ 5 6 ♮ 5 6 5

139
- tu- o- - rum. Et vi- - tam
- rum.
- rum. Et vi- tam ven- tu- ri sae- cu-
-o- rum. Et vi- tam ven- tu- ri sae- cu-
144
A- - men, a- - -
A- - men, a- -
-li. A- - men, a- - men, a- - men, a-
-li. A- men, a- men, a- men, a- men, a- men,
5 6 4 3 4 3
149
- men, a- - men, a- men.
- - men, a- - men, a- - men, a- men.
- men, a- - men, a- men, a- men.
a- men, a- men, a- men, a- men.
4 3 4 [♯]3

Sanctus

15
Ho- san- na in ex- cel-
cae- li et ter- ra glo- ri- a tu- - a.
-ni sunt cae- li et ter- ra glo- ri- a tu- a. Ho- san- na in ex- cel-
Ho- san- na in ex- cel-
20
- sis, ho- san- na in ex- cel- -
Ho- san- na in ex- cel- sis, ho- san- na in ex-
- sis, ho- san- na in ex- - cel-
- sis, ho- san- na in ex- cel- - -
[6] [6]
25
- sis. Be- - ne- di- - ctus qui
-cel- sis. Be- ne- di- ctus qui ve- -
- sis. Be- ne- di- ctus qui ve-
- sis.
5

31
ve- nit in no- mi- ne Do- mi- ni, in no- mi- ne
- nit in no- - mi- ne Do- mi- ni, in no- mi-
- nit in no- mi- ne Do- mi- ni, in no- mi- ne Do-
36
Do- - mi- ni. Ho- san- na in ex- cel- - sis,
-ne Do- - mi- ni. Ho-
- - mi- ni. Ho- san- na in ex- cel- - sis,
Ho- san- na in ex- cel- - sis, ho-
41
ho- san- na in ex- cel- - - sis.
-san- na in ex- cel- sis, ho- san- na in ex- cel- sis.
ho- san- na in ex- - cel- - sis.
-san- na in ex- cel- - - - sis.

Agnus Dei

83

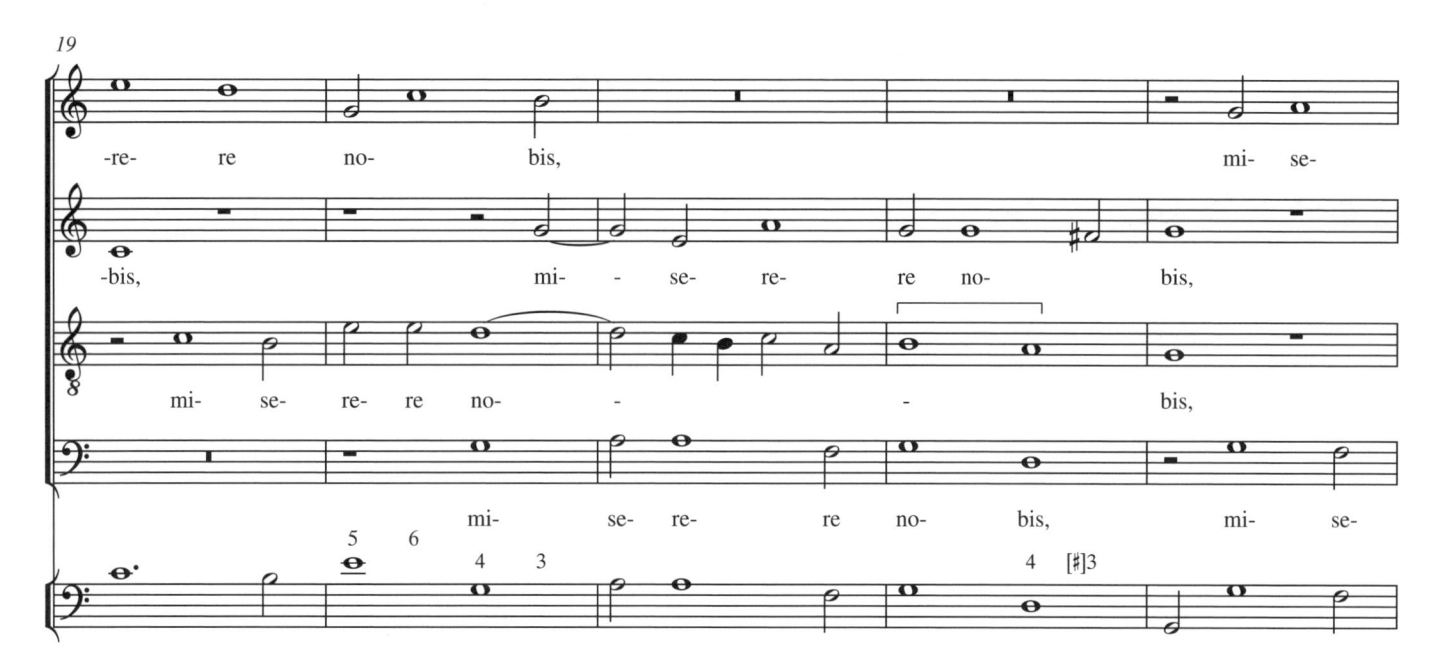

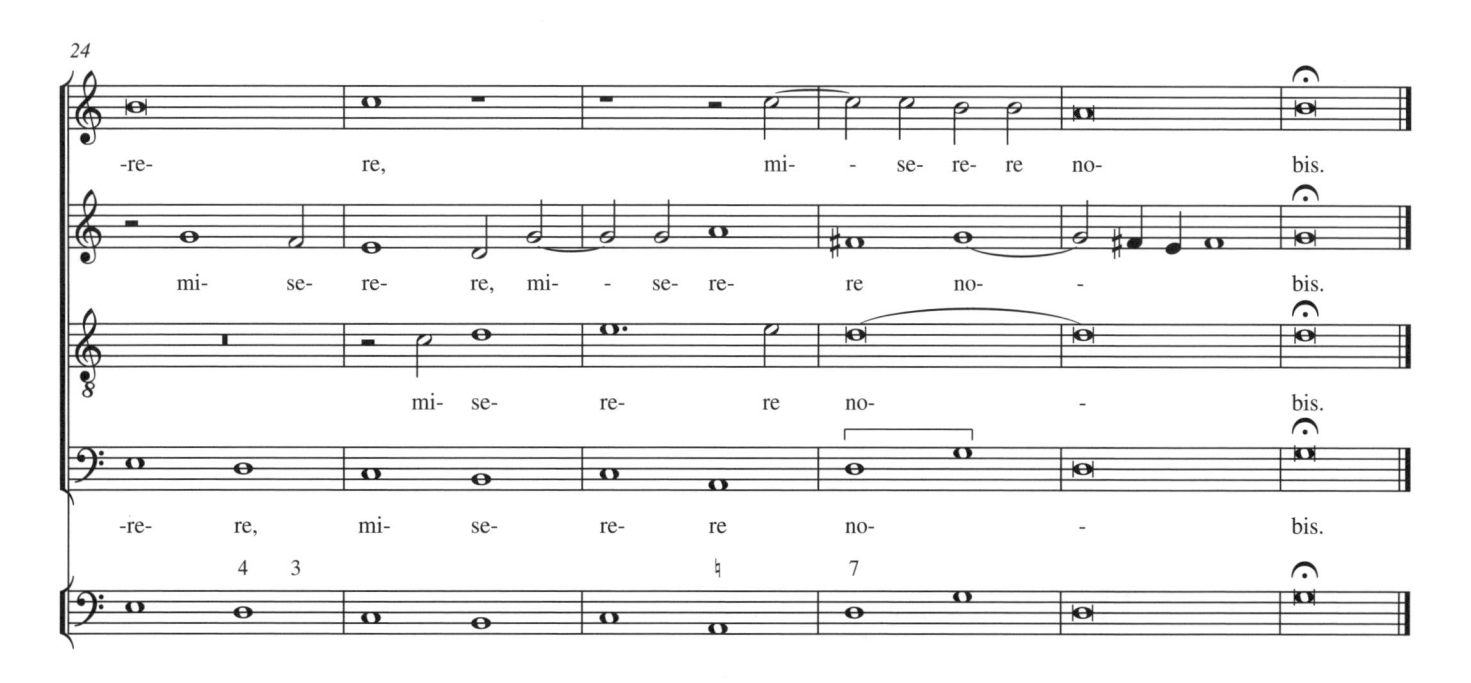

Messa a cappella quarta

Kyrie

16
- i- son. Chri- ste e- le- i- son, e- le- i- son, Chri- ste e-
-le- i- son. Chri- ste e- le- i- son, e- le- i- son,
e- le- i- son. Chri- ste
- i- son. Chri- ste e-
22
-le- i- son, e- le- i- son, Chri- ste e-
Chri- ste e- le- i- son, e- le- i- son,
e- le- i- son, e- le- - - i- son,
-le- i- son, e- le- - - i- son, Chri- ste e-
27
-le- i- son, e- le- i- son, e- le- - i-
Chri- ste e- le- - i- son, e- le- - i-
Chri- ste e- le- i- son, e- le- - i-
-le- - i- son, e- le- - - i-

32
-son. Ky- - ri- e e-
-son. Ky- ri- e, Ky- ri- e e- le- i- son, e- le-
-son. Ky- - ri- e
-son. Ky- ri- e, Ky- ri- e e- - le- i- son, e- le-
5 6 [5] 5
3 4 [4] 3
♭ [6]
38
-le- - i- son, Ky- - ri- e e- le- i-
- i- son, Ky- - ri- e e- le- i-
e- le- - i- son, Ky- - ri- e e- le- i- son, Ky-
- i- son, Ky- - ri- e e- le- i- son, e- le- i-
4 3 [6] 4 [♯]3
43
-son, e- le- i- son, Ky- ri- e
-son, Ky- ri- e e- le- i- son, Ky- ri-
- ri- e e- le- i- son, Ky- ri- e
-son, Ky- ri- e e- le- i- son, Ky- ri-
6

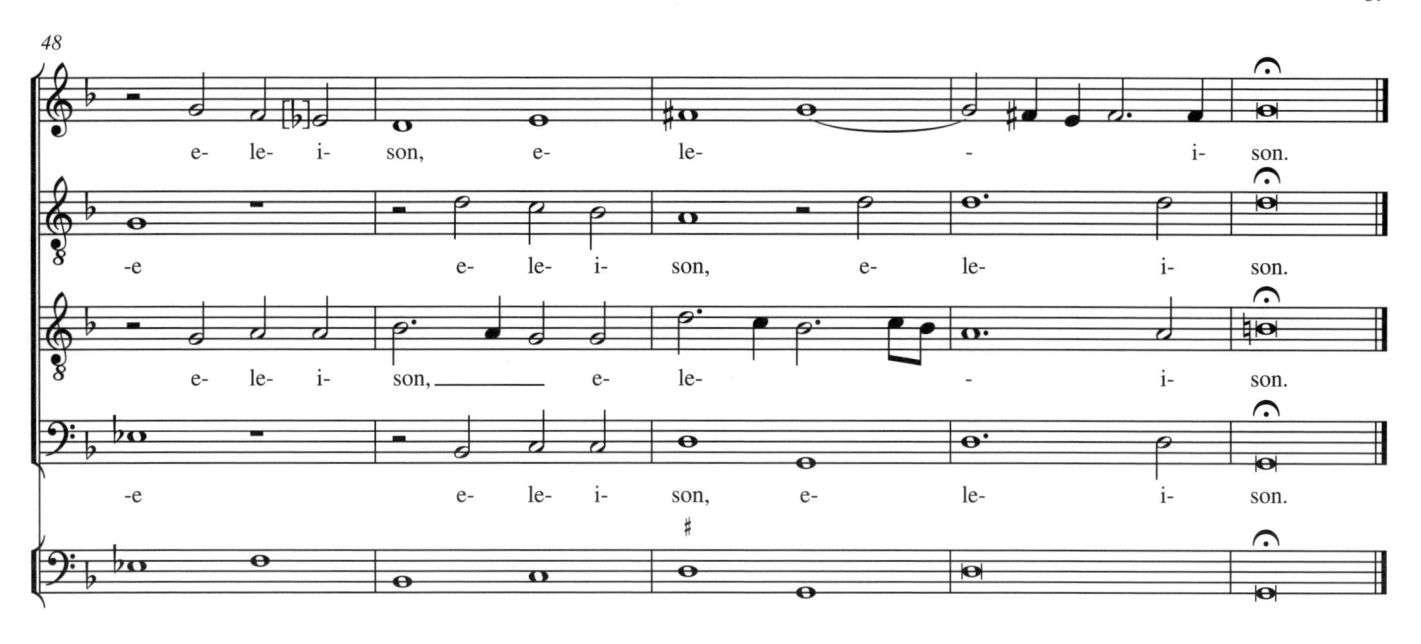

Gloria

10
te. Be- - ne- di- - ci- mus te. Glo- ri- fi-
te. Be- ne- di- ci- mus te. Glo- ri- fi- ca- mus
te. Be- ne- di- ci- mus te. Ad- - o- ra- mus te.
te. Be- ne- di- ci- mus te. Ad- - o- ra- mus te.
[6] ♭
15
-ca- mus te, glo- ri- fi- ca- - mus te. Gra- ti- as a-
te, glo- ri- fi- ca- - mus te. Gra- - ti- as a- gi- mus
Glo- ri- fi- ca- mus te. Gra- ti- as a-
Glo- ri- fi- ca- mus te. Gra- ti- as a-
♭ 6 4 [♯]3 ♭
20
-gi- mus ti- - bi
ti- bi pro- pter ma- gnam glo- - - ri-
-gi- mus ti- - bi
-gi- mus ti- bi pro- pter ma- gnam glo- -
♭6 4 3

25
Do- mi- ne De- - us, Rex cae- le-
-am tu- - am. Do- mi- ne De- us, Rex cae- le-
Do- mi- ne De- us, Rex cae- le-
- ri- am tu- am.
6 4 [♯]3
30
- stis, De- - us Pa- ter om- ni- po- tens.
- stis, De- us Pa- - ter om- ni- po- tens. Do- mi- ne
- stis, De- us Pa- - ter om- ni- po- tens. Do- - mi- ne
De- us Pa- - ter om- ni- po-tens. Do- mi- ne
4 [♮]3 4 3 6
35
u- ni- ge- ni- te Je- - su Chri-
Fi- - li u- ni- ge- ni- te Je- - su Chri-
Fi- - li u- ni- ge- ni- te Je- su Chri-
Fi- - li u- ni- ge- ni- te Je- - su Chri-
5 6 5 6 [6] 4 3

40
-ste. Fi- li- us Pa- -
-ste. Do- mi- ne De- us, A- gnus De- - - i
- ste. Fi- li- us Pa-
-ste. Do- mi- ne De- us, A- gnus De- i, Fi- li- us Pa-
45
- - tris. Qui tol- - lis
Qui tol- - - -
- tris. pec- ca- ta mun-
- tris. pec- ca- ta mun- - - di,
50
pec- ca- ta mun- di, mi- - se- re- re no-
-lis mi- se- re- re no- -
- - di Qui
mi- - se- re- re no- bis.

55
- bis. su-
- - bis. su- sci-
tol- lis pec- ca- ta mun- - di
Qui tol- lis pec- ca- ta mun- di, su-
4 3
60
- sci- pe de- pre- ca- ti- o- nem no- - stram. Qui se-
-pe de- pre- ca- ti- o- nem no- - stram. Qui se-
Qui se-
- sci- pe Qui se- -
4 [♯]3
65
- des mi- - se- re-
- des ad de- - xte- ram Pa- - tris
- des ad de- xte- ram Pa- - tris, mi- se-
- des ad de- xte- - ram Pa- - tris
[♭]7 6 [5] 5
3 4 [4] 3

70
- re no- - bis. Tu so- lus
Quo- - ni- am tu so- lus san-
-re- re no- bis. Quo- ni- am tu so- lus san- ctus. Tu so- lus
Quo- - ni- am tu so- lus san- -
7 6 [♭] [♮] 7 6 4 [♯]3 4 [♯]3
75
Do- mi- nus. Tu so- - lus Je- su
-ctus. Tu so- lus Do- mi- nus. Al- tis- si- mus, Je- su
Do- mi- nus. Tu so- - lus Al- tis- si- mus, Je-
-ctus. Tu so- lus Do- mi- nus. Al- tis- si- mus, Je- su
♮ 6
80
Chri- - ste. in glo-
Chri- - ste. in glo- - ri-
- su Chri- ste. Cum San- cto Spi- - ri- tu,
Chri- - ste. Cum San- cto Spi- - ri- tu,
4 3 [6] 7 6 6 5 ♯

85
- - - ri- a
-a, in glo- ri- a, in glo- ri- a
in glo- - ri- a, in glo-
in glo- - ri- a, in
90
De- i Pa- tris. A- - men,
De- - i Pa- tris. A- men,
- - ri- a A-
glo- - ri- a A-
95
a- - - - men, a-
a- - men, a- men, a-
- - men, a-
- - men, a-

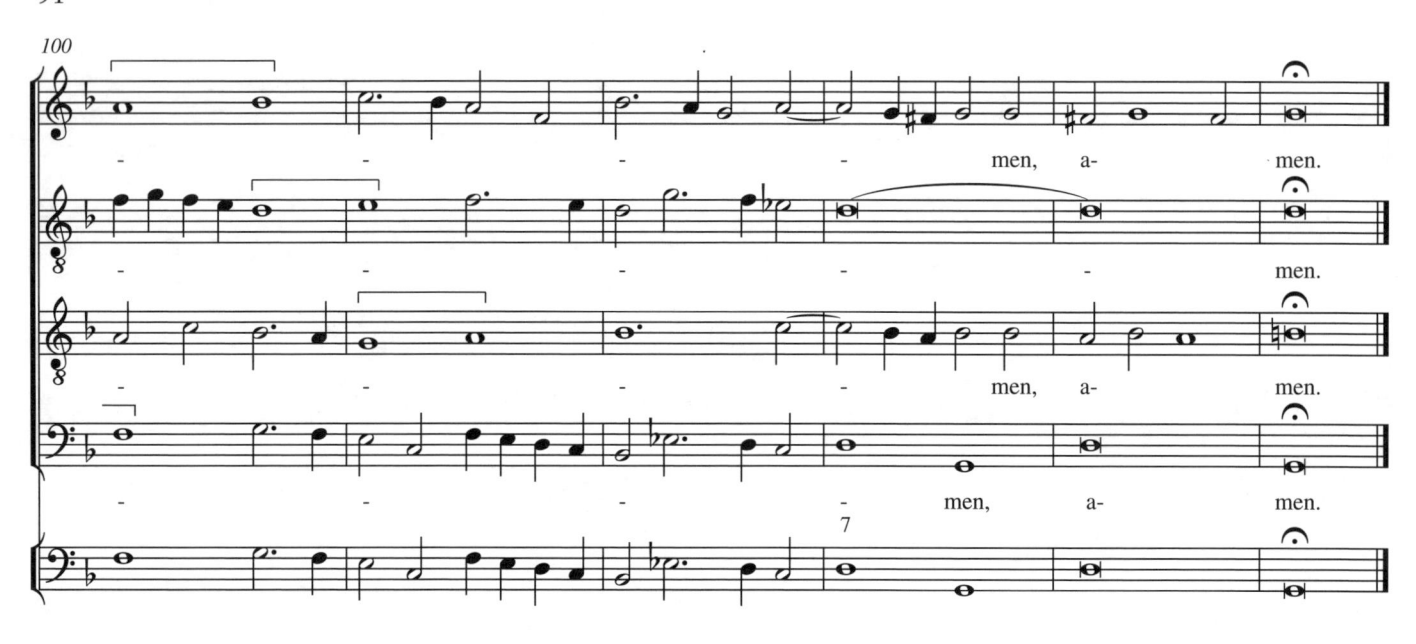

Credo

-bi- li- um. Et in u- num Do- mi- num
-vi- si- bi- li- um. Je- - sum Chri-
Et in u- num Do- - mi- num Je-
Et in u- num Do- mi- num Je- sum Chri-
Fi- li- um De- i u- - ni- ge- ni- tum. Et ex
- stum, Fi- li- um De- - i u- ni- ge- ni- tum. Et ex
- sum Chri- stum, Fi- li- um De- i u- ni- ge- ni- tum.
-stum, Fi- li- um De- i Et ex
Pa- tre na- - tum an- te om-
Pa- tre na- - tum De- um de
an- te om- ni- a sae- cu- la.
Pa- tre na- - tum an- te om- ni- a sae- cu- la.

25
-ni- a sae- cu- la. De- um de De- o, lu- men de lu- mi-
De- - o, lu- men de lu- mi- ne, [de lu- mi-
lu- men de lu- mi- ne, lu- men de lu- mi- ne,
De- um de De- o, lu- men de lu- - mi- ne,
6 6 6
30
-ne, De- um ve- rum de De- o ve- ro, de De- o ve- ro,
-ne,] De- - um ve- rum de De- o ve- ro, de De- o
De- um ve- rum de De- o ve- ro, de
De- um ve- rum de De- o ve- - ro, de
4 3
35
de De- o ve- ro. con- sub-
ve- - ro. Ge- ni- tum, non fa- ctum, con-
De- o ve- ro. Ge- ni- tum, non fa- ctum,
De- o ve- ro. Ge- ni- tum, non fa- - ctum,
4 [♯]3 [6] 5 6

41
-stan- ti- a- lem Pa- tri: per quem om- - ni- a fa- cta
- sub- stan- ti- a- lem Pa- tri: per quem om- ni- a fa- - cta sunt.
per quem om- ni- a fa- cta
per quem om- ni- a, om- ni- a fa- cta
46
sunt. de-
et pro- pter no- stram sa- lu- tem
sunt. Qui pro- pter nos ho- mi- nes, et pro- pter no- stram sa- lu- tem de-
sunt. Qui pro- pter nos ho- mi- nes, et pro- pter no- stram sa- lu- tem de-
51
-scen- dit de cae- - - -
de- scen- - dit de cae- - -
-scen- dit de cae- lis, de- scen- dit de cae-
-scen- dit de cae- lis, de- scen- dit de cae-

56
lis. Et in- car- na- tus est de Spi- ri- tu
lis. Et in- car- na- tus est de Spi-
lis. Et in- car- na- tus est de Spi- ri- tu
lis. Et in- car- na- tus est de Spi- ri- tu
4 [♯]3
61
San- cto ex Ma- ri- a Vir- gi- ne: et ho- mo fa-
-ri- tu San- cto ex Ma- ri- a Vir- gi- ne: et ho- mo, ho- mo
San- cto ex Ma- ri- a Vir- gi- ne: et ho- mo fa-
San- cto ex Ma- ri- a Vir- gi- ne: et ho- mo
5 6
66
ctus est.
fa- ctus est. Cru- ci- fi- xus e- ti- am pro no-
ctus est. Cru- ci- fi- xus e- ti- am pro no-
fa- ctus est.
5 ♭6 5 [6] ♭6 6 5 6

72
e- ti- am pro no- bis: sub
- - bis, e- ti- am pro no-
- - - bis, e- ti- am pro no-
4 [♯]3
77
Pon- ti- o Pi- la- to pas- sus, et se- pul-
-bis: sub Pon- ti- o Pi- la- - to pas- - sus, et se- pul-
-bis: sub Pon- ti- o Pi- la- - to pas- sus, et se- pul- tus
[♭]4 3
82
- tus est. ter- ti- a di-
- tus est. Et re- sur- re- - xit ter- ti- a
est. Et re- sur- re- - xit ter- ti- a
6 5
[4 ♮3]
5 6 ♭6 5 [6] 6 ♭6 6 5 6

87
- e, se- cun- dum Scri- ptu- - ras.
di- e, se- cun- dum Scri- ptu- - ras. Et a- scen-
di- e, se- cun- dum Scri- ptu- - ras. Et a-
92
se- det ad de- xte-
-dit in cae- - lum: se- det ad de- xte-
-scen- dit in cae- - lum: se- det ad de- xte-
97
-ram Pa- - - tris. ven- tu- rus est cum glo-
-ram Pa- - - tris. Et i- te- rum ven- tu- rus est cum
-ram Pa- - - tris. Et i- te- rum

102
-ri- a, ju- di- ca- re vi- vos et mor- - tu-
glo- ri- a, ju- di- ca- re vi- vos et mor- - tu-
ju- di- ca- re vi- vos, vi- vos et mor- - tu-
4 3 6
107
-os: cu- jus re- gni non e- rit fi- nis, non e- rit
-os: cu- jus re- gni non e- rit fi- nis, non e- rit
-os: cu- jus re- gni non e- rit fi- nis, non e- rit
112
fi- nis, non e- rit fi- nis. Et in Spi- ri-
fi- nis, non e- rit fi- nis.
fi- nis, non e- rit fi- nis. Et in
Et in
6

117
-tum San- ctum, Do- - mi- num, et vi- vi- fi- can-
et vi- vi- fi- can- -
Spi- ri- tum San- ctum, Do- - mi- num, et vi- - vi- fi-
Spi- ri- tum San- ctum, Do- - mi- num, et vi- vi- fi- can-
5 6 5 6 5 6 ♯
122
- tem: qui ex Pa- tre Fi- li- o- que pro- ce-
- tem: qui ex Pa- tre Fi- li- o- que pro- ce-
-can- tem: qui ex Pa- tre Fi- li- o- que pro- ce-
-tem: qui ex Pa- tre Fi- li- o- que pro- ce-
4 3 4 3 6 7 3 7 [♯]3 6 4
127
- dit. Qui cum Pa- tre et Fi- - li- o si- mul
- dit.
- dit. Qui cum Pa- - tre et Fi- li- o si- - mul ad- o-
- dit. Qui cum Pa- tre et Fi- - li- o si- mul
[5] [4] 5 [♯]3 5 6 [6]

132
ad- o- ra- tur, et con- glo- ri- fi- ca- -
-ra- - - tur, et con- glo- ri- fi- ca-
ad- o- ra- tur, et con- glo- ri- fi- ca- - tur:
4 3
137
-tur: qui lo- cu- tus est per Pro- phe- - tas. Et u- nam san-
Et u- nam san- ctam ca-
-tur: qui lo- cu- tus est per Pro- phe- - tas. Et u- nam san-
qui lo- cu- tus est per Pro- phe- - tas.
4 3 6 5
142
-ctam ca- tho- li- cam et a- po- sto- li- cam Ec- cle- - si-
-tho- li- cam et a- po- sto- li- cam Ec- cle- - si-
-ctam ca- tho- li- cam et a- po- sto- li- cam Ec- cle- si-
et a- po- sto- li- cam
6 5 [6] ♮ ♭ 5 6 4 [♯]3

147
-am. Con- fi- - te- or in
-am. Con- fi- te- or u- num ba- pti- - sma
-am. Con- fi- te- or u- num ba- pti- - sma in
Con- fi- te- or u- num ba- pti- sma
♮ 7 6 4 [♯]3 5 6 4 [♯]3
152
re- mis- si- o- nem pec- ca- to- -
in re- mis- si- o- nem pec- - ca- to- -
re- mis- si- o- nem pec- ca- to- -
in re- mis- si- o- nem pec- ca- to- -
157
-rum. Et ex- spe- - - cto re-
-rum. Et ex- spe- - - - cto re-
-rum. Et ex- spe- - - - cto re-
-rum. Et ex- spe- - - cto re-
5 6 4 3

162
- sur- re- cti- o- nem mor- tu- o- -
- sur- re- cti- o- - nem
- sur- re- cti- o- - nem mor- - tu- o- -
- sur- re- cti- o- nem mor- - tu- o- -
4 3 4 [♯]3
167
-rum.
Et vi- tam ven- tu- ri sae- cu- li. A- men,
-rum. Et vi- - tam ven- tu- ri sae- cu- li. A- - men, a-
-rum. ven- tu- ri sae- cu- li.
5 6 ♭6
172
A- - - men, a-
a- men, a- -
- men, a- - - -
A- - - men, a- men, a-
4 3 5 6 4 [♯]3 [6]

Sanctus

8
Do- mi-nus De- us Sa- ba- oth.
- ctus Do- mi-nus De- us Sa- -
- ctus Do- - mi-nus De- us
- ctus, San- - - ctus
4 3 ♮ ♭
13
Ple- ni sunt cae- li et ter- - -
- ba- oth. Ple- ni sunt cae- li et ter- ra, et ter-
Sa- ba- oth. Ple- ni sunt cae- li et ter-
Ple- ni sunt cae- li et ter- - -
♭6
18
- ra glo- -
- ra glo- - ri- a,
- ra glo- - ri- a, glo-
-ra glo- -
4 3 [6] ♭6

22
-ri- a tu- - - a. Ho- san-
glo- ri- a tu- a. Ho- san- na
- ri- a, glo- ri- a tu- a.
- ri- a, glo- - ri- a tu- - a. Ho- san- na in ex-
26
- na in ex- cel- - - sis, ho- san- na
in ex- cel- - sis, in ex- cel- sis, ho- san-
Ho- san- - na in ex- cel- -
-cel- - - - sis, ho- san-
4 [♯]3
4 3
31
in ex- cel- - sis.
-na in ex- cel- sis. Be- ne- di-
-sis, in ex- cel- - sis.
-na in ex- cel- sis. Be- ne- di-
♭6 5

37
qui ve- - nit in no- mi- ne
- - ctus qui ve- nit in no- mi- ne Do- -
- ctus qui ve- nit in no- mi- ne Do- -
7 6 6 5 4 [♯]3 ♮
42
Do- mi- ni, in no- mi- ne Do- - - mi- ni, in
- mi- ni, in no- mi- ne Do- - mi- ni, in no- mi- ne
- mi- ni, in no- mi- ne Do- mi- ni, in no- mi- ne
♭ 4 3 4 [♯]3 [6]
47
no- mi- ne Do- - mi- ni. Ho- san- na, ho- san- na
Do- - mi- ni. Ho- san- - na, ho- san- na
Do- - mi- ni. Ho- san- na, ho- san- na
4 3

Agnus Dei

A- gnus De-
gnus De-
i,
i, qui tol- lis pec- ca- ta mun- di: mi- se-
pec- ca- ta mun- di:
pec- ca- ta mun- di: mi- se- re-
mi- se- re- re no-
re no- bis,
-re- re no- bis, mi- se- re- re no-

20
- bis, mi- se- re- re
mi- se- re- re no- - bis,
- bis, mi- se- re- re no- bis,
-bis, mi- - se- re- re no- bis, mi- - se- re- re no-
4 [♯]3 5 6 4 [♯]3 2
25
no- - bis, mi- - se- re- re no- bis.
mi- se- re- re no- bis, mi- - se- re- - re no- bis.
mi- - se- re- re no- - bis.
- bis, mi- se- re- re no- - bis.
4 3 4 [♯]3 ♮ 4 [♯]3 ♮

Messa a cappella quinta

Kyrie

13
- ri- e e- le- - - i- son.
-son, Ky- - ri- e e- le- - i- son.
-le- i- son, Ky- - ri- e e- le- - i- son.
Ky- - ri- e e- le- - i- son.
4 [♯]3
18
Chri- ste e- le- i- son,
Chri- ste e- le- i- son, Chri-
Chri- ste, Chri- ste e- le- i- son, e- le- i- son, Chri- ste
Chri- ste, Chri- ste e- le- i- son, Chri- - ste e- le- i- son, Chri- ste e- le- i- son, Chri-
♯ [6] 4 [♯]3
23
Chri- - ste e- le- - i- son,
-ste e- le- i- son, Chri- ste e- le- - i- son, e-
e- le- i- son, Chri- ste e- le- i- son, Chri- ste e- le- i- son,
-ste e- le- i- son, Chri- ste e- le- i- son, e-
4 3 4 3 4 [♯]3

28
e- le- i- son, Chri- ste, Chri- ste e- le- i- son,
-le- i- son, Chri- ste e- le- - i- son,
e- le- i- son, Chri- ste, Chri- ste e- le- i-
-le- i- son, Chri- ste, Chri- ste e- le- i- son, Chri- ste e- le- i-
4 [♯]3 5 [6] [6]
33
e- le- - i- son,
e- le- i-
-son, e- le- i- son, Chri- ste e- le- i- son, e- le- i- son,
-son, e- le- i- son, Chri- ste e- le- i- son, e- le-
[♮] ♯ 6 4 3 6
38
e- le- - i- son, Chri- ste e- le- i- son.
-son, e- le- - i- son, e- le- i- son.
e- le- - i- son, e- le- - i- son.
- i- son, e- le- i- son, Chri- ste e- le- i- son.
♯

43
Ky- ri- e e- le- i- son, e- le- i-
Ky- ri- e e- le- i- son, e- le- i-
Ky- ri-
Ky- ri- e e- le- i- son, e- le- i- son, e- le- i- son,
[6]
[7] [♯]3 [6] 4 [5] [4] [5] [♯]3
47
-son, Ky- ri- e,
-son, ⟨Ky- ri- e e- le- i- son,⟩ e- le- -
-e e- le- i- son, Ky- ri- e e- le-
Ky- ri- e e- le- -
6
4 3
51
Ky- ri- e e- le- i- son.
- - i- son, Ky- - ri- e e- le- i- son.
- - i- son, Ky- - ri- e e- le- i- son.
- i- son, Ky- - ri- e e- le- i- son.
4 3 4 [♯]3
7 [♯]3 6 4 [5] [4] 5 [♯]3

Gloria

16
-bi glo- - - ri- am tu-
-bi glo- ri- am tu- -
-bi pro- pter ma- gnam glo- ri- am, glo- ri- am tu- - am.
-bi pro- pter ma- gnam glo- ri- am
4 3
21
-am. Rex cae- le- stis, De- us Pa- ter om-
-am. Rex cae- le- stis, De- us Pa- - ter om- ni-
Do- mi- ne De- us, Rex cae- le- stis, De- us Pa- ter om- ni- po- tens.
Do- mi- ne De- us, De- us Pa- ter om-
4 3
27
-ni- po- tens. u- - ni- ge- ni- te Je- su, Je-
- po- tens. Do- mi- ne Fi- li Je- - su, Je- - su, Je-
Do- mi- ne Fi- li u- ni- ge- - ni- te Je-
-ni- po- tens. u- ni- ge- ni- te Je- - su, Je-
6 6 7 6 6 4 3

32
-su Chri- - ste. Do- mi- ne De- us, A- gnus De- -
- su Chri- ste. Do- mi- ne De- us, A- gnus De- -
-su Chri- - ste. Fi- li- us
- su Chri- ste. Do- mi- ne De- us, A- gnus De- - i
[6] 4 [♯]3
37
-i, Fi- li- us Pa- - - tris. Qui
- i, Fi- li- us Pa- - tris. Qui tol-
Pa- - - - -
Qui tol-
[6] 4 3 4 [♯]3
42
tol- - - -
- - - - lis pec-
- tris.
-lis, qui tol- - - lis pec-
♯ 6 ♯

46
-lis pec- ca- - ta mun- di
-ca- ta mun- di, mi- se- re- re no- bis,
pec- ca- ta mun- di, mi- se- re- re no- bis, mi- se- re-
-ca- ta mun- di, mi- se- re- re no- - -
5 ♯6 4 [♯]3 6 7 5 6
52
Qui tol- lis pec- ca- ta mun- di,
mi- se- re- re no- bis. Qui tol- lis pec- ca- ta mun-
-re no- - bis. pec- ca- ta mun- di,
-bis, mi- se- re- re no- bis. Qui tol- lis
4 3 4 3
57
su- sci- pe de- pre- ca- ti- o- nem no- stram, de- pre-
-di, su- sci- pe de- pre- ca- ti- o- - nem no- stram.
su- sci- pe de- pre- ca- ti- o- nem no- stram, de- - pre- ca-
su- sci- pe de- pre- ca- ti- o- - nem no- stram, de- pre-
♮ ♯ 7 3 6 4 3 ♯

62
-ca- ti- o- nem no- - stram. Qui se- des
Qui se- des ad de- xte- ram Pa-
- ti- o- nem no- - stram. Qui se- des ad de- xte- ram Pa-
-ca- ti- o- nem no- - stram. Qui se- des
67
ad de- xte- ram Pa- tris, mi- - se- re- re no- bis. Quo- - ni- am
- - tris, mi- - se- re- re no- bis. Quo- - ni- am tu
- - tris, mi- se- re- re no- bis. Quo- ni- am tu
mi- se- re- re no- - bis. Quo- ni- am
72
Tu so- - lus Do- mi- nus.
so- lus san- ctus. Tu so- - lus Do- mi- nus. Tu so- - lus Al-
so- lus san- ctus. Tu so- - lus Al-
Tu so- lus Do- - mi- nus. Tu so- lus Al-

77
Je- - su, Je- su Chri- - ste. Cum San- cto
-tis- si- mus, Je- - su, Je- - su Chri- - ste.
-tis- si- mus, Je- - su, Je- - su Chri- ste.
-tis- si- mus, Je- - su, Je- - su Chri- - ste. Cum San- cto
4 [♯]3 5 7 6 [5] 5 [♯]3 4 [4] [♯]3 5 6
82
Spi- ri- tu, in glo- ri- a De- - i Pa- tris. A- -
in glo- ri- a De- - i Pa- tris. A- -
in glo- ri- a De- - i Pa- tris. A- -
Spi- ri- tu, De- i Pa- tris. A- men, a- -
5 6 ♮ ♯ ♯
87
-men, a- - men, a- men, a- men, a- men, a- men.
-men, a- - men, a- - men, a- - men, a- men.
-men, a- - men, a- men, a- men, a- men, a- men.
-men, a- - men, a- men, a- men, a- men, a- men.
6

Credo

15
-ge- ni- tum. an- te om- ni- a sae- cu- la.
u- ni- ge- ni- tum. De- um de
Et ex Pa- tre na- tum an- te om- ni- a sae- cu- la. De-
Et ex Pa- tre na- tum an- te om- ni- a sae- cu- la.
20
lu- men de lu- mi- ne, de De- - o ve-
De- o, De- - um ve- - rum de De- o ve-
-um de De- o, De- um ve- rum de De- o ve-
lu- men de lu- mi- ne, de De- - o ve-
25
- ro. Ge- - ni- tum, non fa- ctum, con- sub- stan- ti- a- lem
- ro. Ge- - ni- tum, non fa- ctum, con- sub- stan- ti- a- lem
- ro. Ge- - ni- tum, non fa- - ctum, con- - sub- stan- ti-
- ro. Ge- - ni- tum, non fa- ctum, con- sub- stan- ti- a- lem

30
Pa- tri: per quem om- ni- a fa- - cta sunt.
Pa- tri Qui pro-
-a- lem Pa- tri: per quem om- ni- a fa- cta sunt. Qui
Pa- tri: per quem om- ni- a fa- cta sunt. Qui
35
et
- pter nos ho- - - - mi- nes,
pro- pter nos ho- - - mi-
pro- pter nos ho- - - mi-
40
pro- pter no- stram sa- lu- - tem de- scen-
et pro- pter no- stram sa- lu- tem de- scen- - dit de
-nes, et pro- pter no- stram sa- lu- tem de- scen- dit de
-nes, et pro- pter no- stram sa- lu- tem

45
-dit de cae- lis. Et in- car- na- tus est ex Ma-
cae- lis. de Spi- ri- tu San- cto
cae- lis. Et in- car- na- - tus est de Spi- ri- tu San-
Et in- car- na- tus est ex Ma-
50
-ri- a Vir- gi- ne Cru- ci- - fi- xus e- ti-
et ho- mo fa- - ctus est. Cru- ci- fi- xus e- ti-
- cto et ho- mo fa- ctus est. Cru- ci- fi- xus e- ti-
-ri- a Vir- gi- ne: et ho- mo fa- ctus est. Cru- ci- fi- xus e- ti-
56
-am pro no- - bis: pas- -
-am pro no- bis: pas- -
-am pro no- bis: sub Pon- ti- o Pi- la- to pas- -
-am pro no- bis: sub Pon- ti- o Pi- la- to pas- -

127

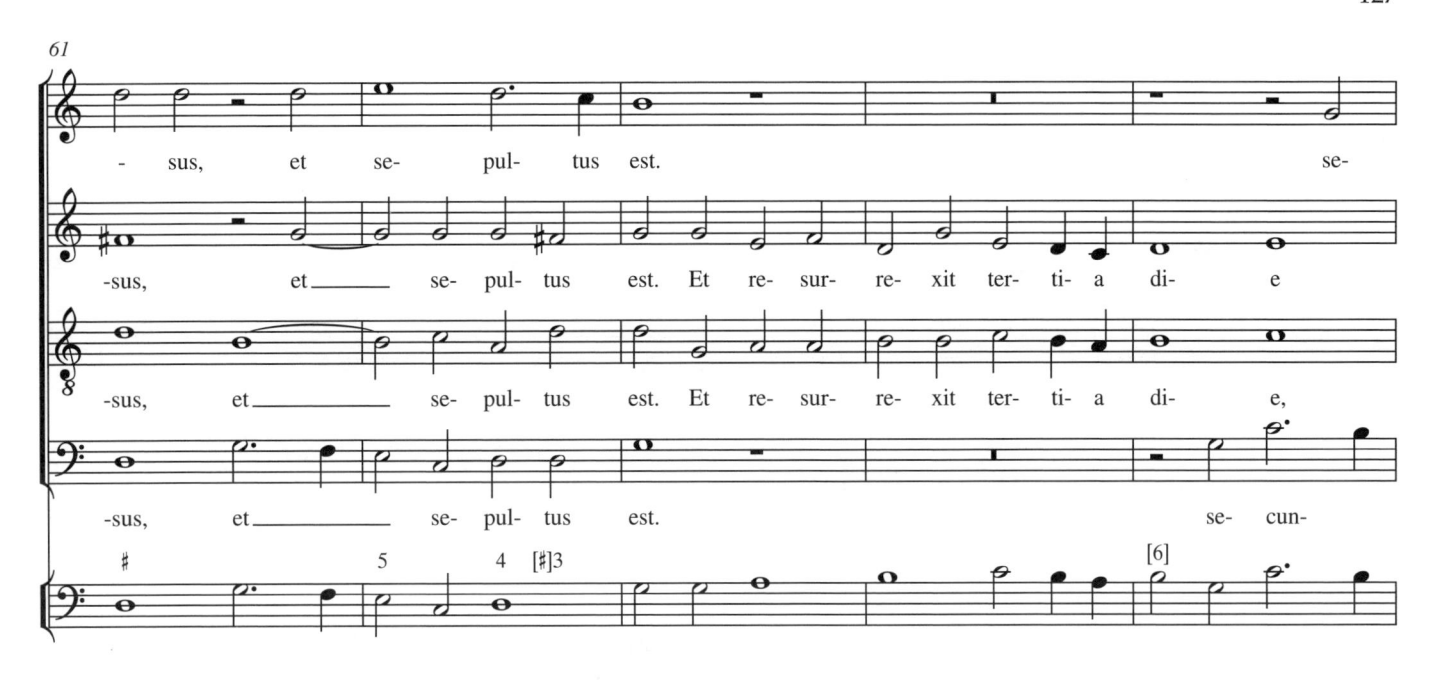

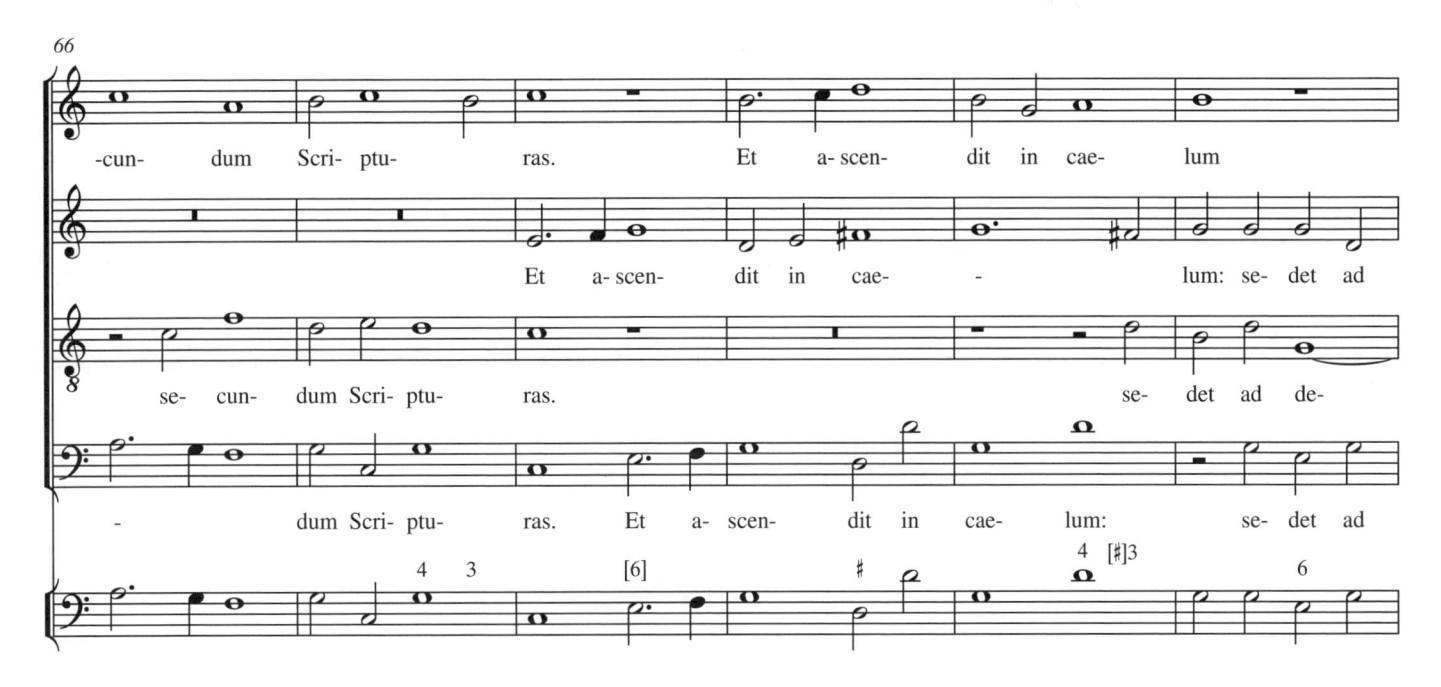

77
glo- ri- a, cu- jus re- gni non e- rit
glo- ri- a, ju- di- ca- re vi- vos et mor- tu- os: cu- jus re- gni
ju- di- ca- re vi- vos et mor- tu- os: cu- jus re- gni non
ju- di- ca- re vi- vos et mor- tu- os: cu- jus re- gni non
83
fi- nis, non e- rit fi- nis, non, non e- rit fi- nis.
non e- rit fi- nis, non, non e- rit fi-
e- rit fi- nis, non e- rit fi- nis, non, non e- rit fi-
e- rit fi- nis, non e- rit fi- nis, non, non e- rit fi-
89
et vi- vi- fi-
-nis. Et in Spi- ri- tum San- ctum, Do- mi- num, et vi- vi- fi-
-nis. Et in Spi- ri- tum San- ctum, Do- mi- num,
-nis. et vi- vi- fi- can-

-can- tem Qui cum Pa- tre et Fi- li- o si- mul ad- o- ra-

-can- tem: qui ex Patre Fi- li- o- que pro- ce- dit. si- mul ad- o- ra-

qui ex Patre Fi- li- o- que pro- ce- dit. Qui cum Pa- tre et Fi- li- o si- mul ad- o- ra-

-tem: qui ex Patre Fi- li- o- que pro- ce- dit. Qui cum Pa- tre et Fi- li- o si- mul ad- o- ra-

-tur, et con- glo- ri- fi- ca- tur: qui lo- cu- tus est per Prophe- tas. Et

-tur, et con- glo- ri- fi- ca- tur: qui lo- cu- tus est per Prophe- tas. Et

-tur, et con- glo- ri- fi- ca- tur: qui lo- cu- tus est per Prophe- tas. Et

-tur, et con- glo- ri- fi- ca- tur: qui lo- cu- tus est per Prophe- tas.

110
u- nam san- ctam ca- tho- li- cam et a- po- sto- li- cam Ec- cle- si-
u- nam san- ctam ca- tho- li- cam et a- po- sto- li- cam Ec- cle- si-
u- nam san- ctam ca- tho- li- cam et a- po- sto- li- cam Ec- cle- si-
6
4 [♯]3
115
-am. Con- fi- te- or u- num ba- pti- sma in re- mis- si- o- - nem pec- ca-
-am. Con- fi- - te- or u- num ba- pti- sma in re- mis- si- o- - nem pec- ca-
-am. Con- fi- te- or u- num ba- pti- sma in re- mis- si- o- nem pec- ca- to-
Con- fi- te- or u- num ba- pti- sma in re- mis- si- o- - nem pec- ca-
♮ ♯ 5 ♯
121
- to- rum. Et ex- spe- cto, ⟨et ex- spe- cto⟩
-to- rum. Et ex- spe- cto, ⟨et ex- spe- cto⟩
- rum. Et ex- spe- cto, ⟨et ex- spe- cto⟩ re- sur- re- cti-
-to- rum. Et ex- spe- cto, ⟨et ex- spe- cto⟩ re- sur- re- cti-
4 [♯]3
[6]

127
Et
Et vi- -
-o- nem mor- tu- - o- - - rum. Et vi-
-o- nem mor- tu- o- - - rum. Et
132
vi- tam A- -
-tam ven- tu- ri sae- cu- li. A- - men, a-
-tam ven- tu- ri sae- cu- li. A- - men, a- -
vi- tam ven- tu- ri sae- cu- li. A- men, a-
137
- men, a- men, a- men, a- - men, a-
- - men, a- men, a- - men, a-
- men, a- - men, a- men, a- - men, a-
- - men, a- men, a- - men, a-

Sanctus

10
- us Sa- - - ba- oth. Ple-
De- us Sa- - ba- oth.
- - us Sa- ba- oth. Ple- ni sunt cae- li et ter-
De- - us Sa- - ba- oth. Ple- ni sunt cae- li et
15
-ni sunt cae- li et ter- - ra glo- ri- a tu- -
glo- - ri- a tu- -
- - - ra glo- ri- a tu-
ter- - - ra Ho-
20
-a. Ho- san- na in ex- cel- sis,
-a. Ho- san- na in ex- cel- - sis, in ex- cel-
-a. Ho- san- -
-san- - na, ho-

in ex- cel - sis, ho- san-
-sis, ho- san- na in ex- cel- - sis, ho- san- na, ho-
-san- na in ex- cel- sis, in ex- cel- sis, ho- san-
-na in ex- cel- sis. Be- ne- di- ctus
-na in ex- cel- sis. Be- ne- di- ctus qui ve-
-san- na in ex- cel- sis. Be- ne- di- ctus qui ve-
-na in ex- cel- sis.
qui ve- nit in no- mi- ne Do- mi- ni, in no- mi- ne Do-
-nit in no- mi- ne Do- mi- ni, in no- mi- ne Do-
-nit in no- mi- ne Do- mi- ni, in no- mi- ne

40
- mi- ni. Ho- san- na in ex-
- mi- ni. Ho- san- na in ex- cel- - sis,
Do- mi- ni. Ho- san-
Ho- san- - na,
7 6 4 [♯]3
44
-cel- sis, in ex- cel- -
in ex- cel- - - -
- - na in ex- cel- -
ho- san- na in ex- cel- sis, in ex- cel-
[4 3] 4 3
48
-sis, ho- san- - na in ex- cel- sis.
-sis, ho- san- - na in ex- cel- sis.
-sis, ho- san- na, ho- san- na in ex- cel- sis.
-sis, ho- san- na in ex- cel- sis.
6

Agnus Dei

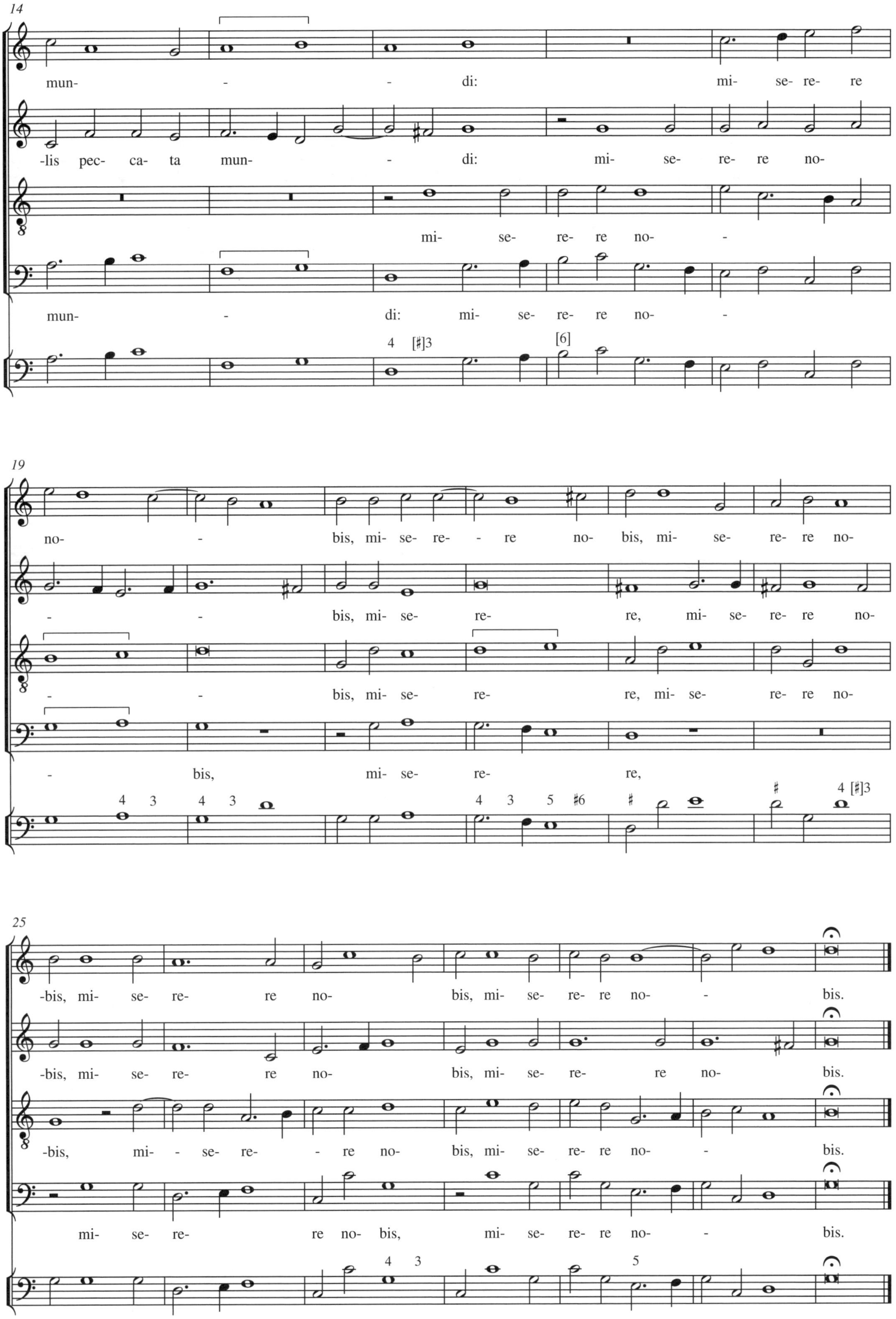

Messa a cappella sesta

Kyrie

139

20
-le- - - i- son.
-le- i- son, e- le- i- son. Chri- ste,
- i- son, e- le- - i- son.
-le- i- son, e- le- i- son.
-e e- le- i- son, e- le- i- son. Chri- ste,
6 2
25
Chri- ste, Chri- ste e- le-
Chri- ste e- le- i- son, e- le- i- son,
Chri- - ste, Chri- ste e- le- i- son, e- le- i- son, Chri-
Chri- - ste, Chri- ste e- le-
Chri- ste e- le- i- son, e- le- i- son,
[6] 7 5 6 6

30
- i- son,
Chri- ste e- le- - i- son, Chri-
-ste e- le- i- son, Chri- ste, Chri- ste e-
- - i- son, Chri- ste e- le- i- son, Chri-
Chri- ste e- le- - i- son, e- le- i-
4 3
35
Chri- ste, Chri- ste e- le- i- son,
-ste, Chri- ste e- le- i- son, e- le- i- son,
-le- i- son, Chri- ste,
- ste, Chri- ste e- le- i- son, e- le- i- son, Chri- ste,
-son, e- le- - i- son, Chri- ste e- le- - i-
4 3 ♮ 4 3

40
Chri- ste e- le- i- son, e- le-
Chri- ste e- le- i- son, e-
Chri- ste e- le- i- son, e- le- i- son, e- le-
Chri- ste e- le- i- son, e- le- i- son, e- le-
-son, Chri- - ste, Chri- ste e- le- i- son, e- le- i- son, e-
6
45
- i- son, e- le- - i- son. Ky- ri- e
-le- i- son, e- le- - i- son. Ky- ri-
- i- son, e- le- - i- son. Ky- ri- e e-
-i- son, e- le- - i- son.
-le- i- son, e- le- - i- son.

50
e- le- i- son, Ky- - ri- e e- le- i- son,
-e e- le- - i- son, Ky- ri- e e- le- i- son,
-le- i- son,
Ky- ri- e e- le- i- son, e- le-
Ky- - ri- e e- le- i- son, e- le-
7 6 5 ♮6
55
e- le- i- son, e- le- i- son,
Ky- ri- e e- le- i- son, e- le- i-
Ky- ri- e e- le- - i- son,
- i- son, e- le- i- son, e- le- i-
- i- son, Ky- ri- e e- le- i- son, e- le- i-
4 [♮]3 7 6 4 [♮]3 5 6 [♮] 6

60
Ky- ri- e e- le- i- son, e- le- i- son, Ky- ri-
-son, Ky- ri- e e- le- - i- son, e- le- i- son,
Ky- ri- e e- le- i- son, e- le- i- son, e- le- i- son, Ky-
-son, e- le- i- son,
-son, e- le- i- son, Ky- ri-
7 6
♭
65
-e e- le- i- son, Ky- ri- e
Ky- - ri- e e- le- i- son, Ky- ri-
- ri- e e- - le- i- son, Ky- ri-
Ky- ri- e e- le- i- son, Ky- ri-
-e e- le- i- son, Ky- ri- e e-
6
7 6 4 [♮]3

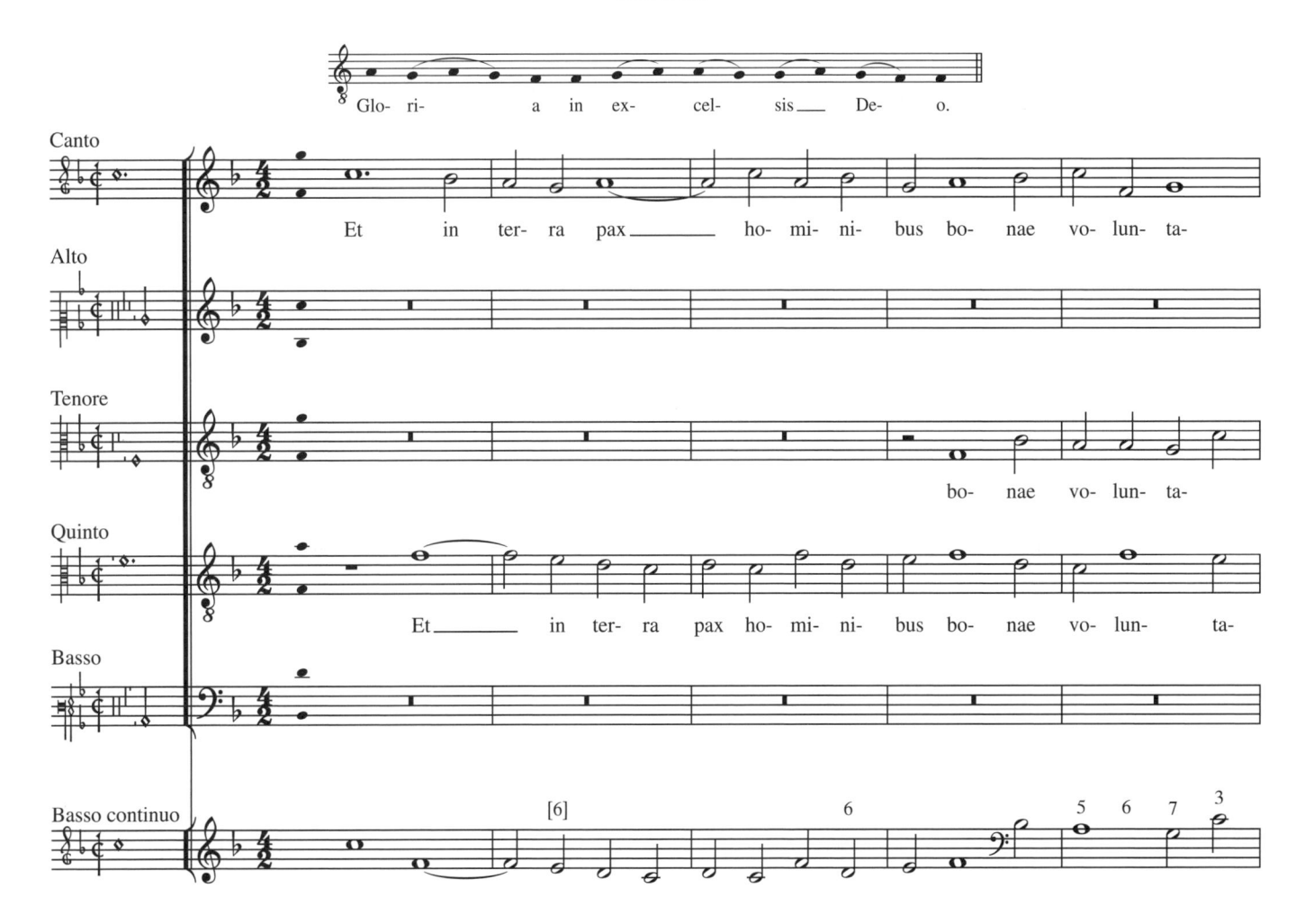

Gloria

6
- - tis. Be- ne- di- ci-
Lau- da- - mus te. Be- - ne- di- ci-
- - tis. Lau- da- mus te. Be- - ne- di- ci-
- - tis. Lau- da- mus te.
Lau- da- mus te. Be- ne- di- ci- mus
11
-mus te. Ad- o- ra- mus te. Glo- ri- fi- ca- mus te. a-
- mus te. Ad- o- ra- mus te. Glo- ri- fi- ca- mus te. Gra- - ti- as
- mus te. Gra- -
Ad- - o- ra- mus te. Glo- ri- fi- ca- mus te.
te. Ad- o- ra- mus te. Glo- ri- fi- ca- mus te.
4 [♮]3 6 5 6

16
-gi- mus ti- - - bi pro-
— a- gi- mus ti- - bi
- ti- as pro- - pter ma- gnam glo- ri- am, glo- - ri- am tu-
a- gi- mus ti- bi pro- - pter ma- gnam
pro- pter ma- gnam glo- - ri- am, glo-
7 6 4 3 6
21
-pter ma- gnam glo- - ri- am tu- - am.
pro- pter ma- gnam glo- ri- am, glo- ri- am tu- am. Do- mi-
- am. Do- mi- ne
glo- ri- am tu- - - am, glo- - ri- am tu- am.
-ri- am tu- - - am, glo- ri- am tu- am. Do- mi-
5 6 6 6 ♮ 4 [♮]3 5 6

26
-ne De- us, Rex cae- le- - - stis, De-
De- us, Rex cae- le- - - stis, De- us Pa- ter om-
-ne De- us, Rex cae- le- - stis, De- us
6 5 6 6 5 6 6
31
Do- mi- ne, Do- mi- ne Fi- li u-
-us Pa- ter om- ni- po- tens. Do- mi- ne Fi- li
-ni- - po- tens. u- ni- ge-
Do- mi- ne Fi- li u- ni-
Pa- ter om- ni- po- tens. u- ni-
7 6 4 3

36
- ni- ge- ni- te Je- su Chri- ste.
Do- mi- ne De- us,
- ni- te Je- - su, Je- su Chri- ste. Do- mi- ne De-
-ge- ni- te Je- - su Chri- - ste.
-ge- ni- te Je- - su Chri- - ste. Do- mi- ne De- us,
4 [♯]3 ♭
41
A- - gnus De- - i, A- -
-us, A- gnus De- - i, Fi-
Fi- li- us
A- gnus De- - - i,

45
- gnus De- i Qui tol- -
-li- us Pa- - - tris. Qui tol-
Pa- - - tris.
Fi- li- us Pa- - tris. Qui tol-
4 [♯]3 ♮
50
pec- ca- - ta, pec- ca- ta mun-
- - - lis pec- ca-
-lis pec- ca- ta mun- di, qui tol- -
Qui tol- - -
- - lis pec- ca- ta mun- di, pec- ca- ta

55
-di, mi- se- re- re no- -
- ta mun- - - di, mi- se- re- re no-
-lis pec- ca- ta mun- di, mi- se- re- - re no-
-lis pec- ca- - ta mun- - di
mun- - di
7 3 6
60
- bis. Qui tol- - -
- bis. Qui tol- lis pec- ca- ta mun- di,
-bis. Qui tol- - lis pec- ca- ta
Qui tol- - - lis pec- ca- ta,
pec- ca- ta,
4 [♮]3 ♭

65
-lis pec- ca- ta mun- di
su- sci- pe, ⟨su- sci- pe⟩ de- pre- ca- ti- o- nem
mun- - di
pec- ca- ta mun- di, su- sci- pe, su- sci- pe de- pre-
pec- ca- ta mun- di
70
Qui se- - des
no- stram. Qui se- - des ad de- xte- ram Pa-
ad de- xte-ram Pa- tris,
-ca- ti- o- nem no- - stram. ad de- xte- ram Pa-
Qui se- - des ad de- xte-ram Pa-

75
mi- se- re- re no- - - bis.
- tris, mi- se- re- re no- - bis.
mi- se- re- - re no- bis.
-tris Quo- ni- am tu
-tris Quo- ni- am tu
7 3 6 4 [♮]3 [6]
80
Tu so- lus Do- mi-
Tu so- lus Do- mi-
Tu so- - lus Do- mi-
so- lus san- - - - ctus.
so- lus san- - - - ctus. Tu so- lus Do- mi-
[6] ♮ [♭] 7 ♮ 4 [♮]3

85
-nus. Je- - su Chri- - ste. Cum
-nus. Je- - su Chri- ste.
-nus. Tu so- lus Al- tis- si- mus, Je- su Chri- ste.
Tu so- lus Al- tis- si- mus, Je- su Chri- ste.
-nus. Tu so- lus Al- tis- si- mus, Je- su Chri- ste.
5 6
90
San- cto Spi- ri- tu, in glo- ri- a De- i Pa- tris. A-
Cum San- - cto Spi- ri- tu, in glo- ri- a
Cum San- cto Spi- ri- tu
in glo- ri- a De- - i Pa- tris. A-
in glo- ri- a De- i Pa- tris. A-
6 ♭ ♮ ♭

155

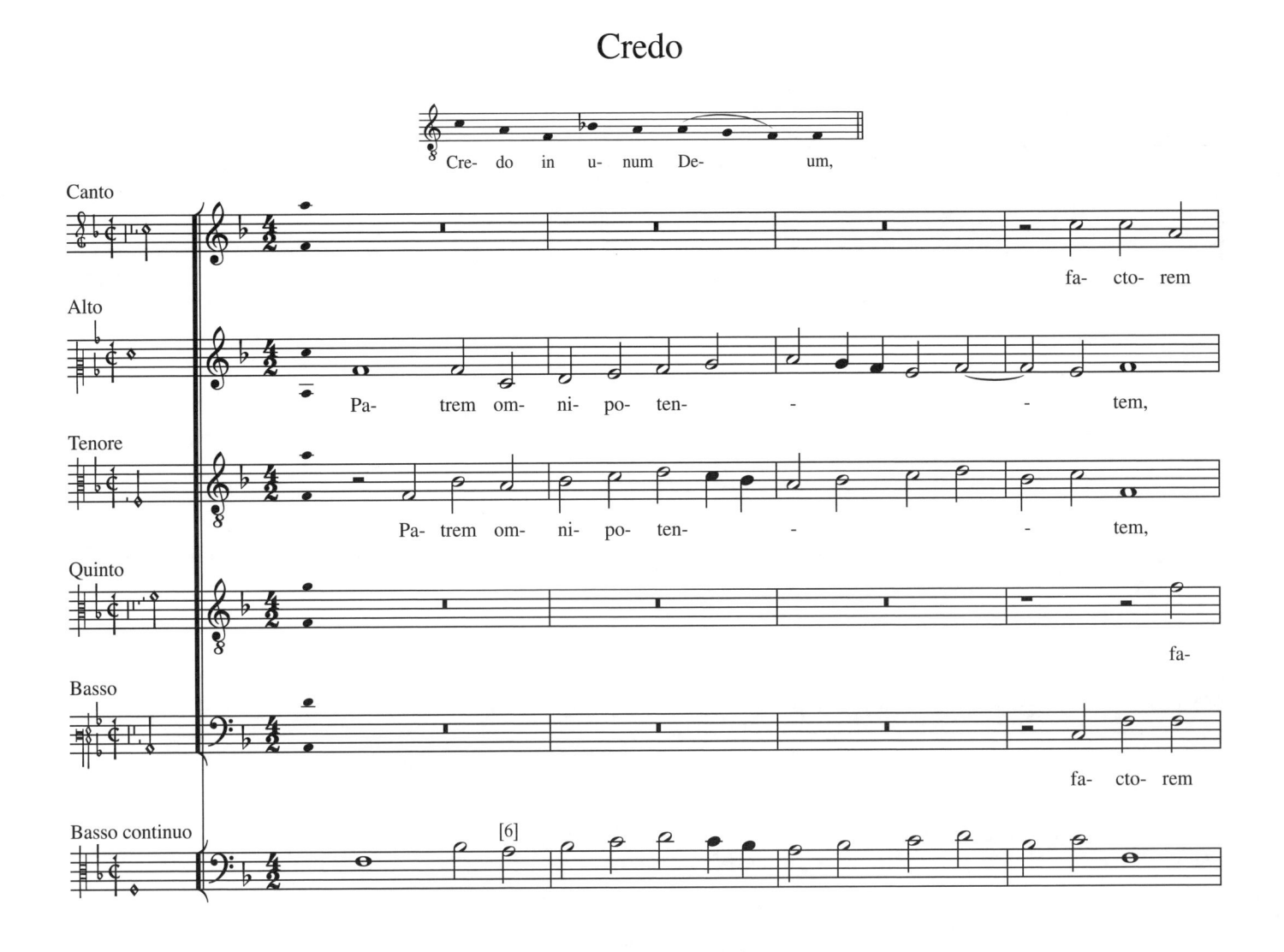

Credo

cae- li et ter- - rae
vi- si- bi- li- um om- ni-
vi- - si- bi- li- um
-cto- rem cae- li et ter- - rae
cae- li et ter- rae,
Et in u- num Do- mi- num Je- sum
-um, et in- vi- si- bi- - li- um. Et in u- num Do- mi-
om- ni- um, et in- vi- si- bi- li- um.
Et in u- num Do- mi- num
et in- vi- si- bi- li- um.

158

25
- te om- ni- a sae- cu- la.
-a sae- - cu- la.
-a, om- ni- - a sae- cu- la. De- um de De- o, lu- men de lu- mi-
De- um de De- o, lu- men de
-a sae- - cu- la. De- um de De- o, lu- men de
4 [♮]3 6
30
De- um ve- rum de De- - o ve- ro. Ge- ni- tum, non fa-
De- um ve- rum de De- o ve- ro. Ge- ni- tum, non fa-
-ne, de De- o ve- ro. Ge- ni- tum, non fa-
lu- mi- ne, de De- o ve- ro.
lu- mi- ne Ge- ni- tum, non fa-
♭ 6 4 3

35
-ctum, con- - sub- stan- ti- a- lem Pa- - tri
- ctum, per quem
- ctum, per quem
con- - sub- stan- ti- a- lem Pa- tri
-ctum, con- - sub- stan- - ti- a- lem Pa- tri: per quem
4 3 4 3
40
Qui pro- pter nos ho- mi- nes
om- ni- a fa- cta sunt. Qui pro- pter nos ho- mi- nes
om- ni- a fa- cta sunt. Qui pro- pter nos ho- mi- nes, et pro- pter
et pro- pter no-
om- ni- a fa- cta sunt.
4 3 6

no- stram sa- lu- tem de- scen- - dit de cae-

-stram sa- lu- tem de- scen- - - dit de cae-

Et in- car- na- tus est de Spi- ri- tu

Et in- car- na- tus est

- lis. Et in- car- na- - tus est de Spi- ri-

- lis. de Spi- ri- tu

Et in- car- na- tus est de Spi- ri- tu

55
San- - cto ex Ma- ri- a Vir- gi- ne: et
ex Ma- ri- a Vir- gi- ne: et ho-
-tu San- - cto et ho-
San- - cto ex Ma- ri- a Vir- gi- ne: et ho- mo
San- - cto ex Ma- ri- a Vir- gi- ne: et
♭ 4 [♯]3
60
ho- mo fa- ctus est. Cru- - ci- fi- xus e- ti- am pro no-
-mo fa- ctus est. Cru- - ci- fi- xus e- ti- am pro no-
- mo fa- ctus est.
fa- ctus est.
ho- mo fa- ctus est. Cru- ci- fi- xus e- ti- am pro no-
4 3 4 3 6

65
- - bis
- - bis
sub Pon- ti- o Pi- la- to pas- sus, et se-
sub Pon- ti- o Pi- la- to pas- sus, et se- pul- tus
- - bis
[6]

70
Et re- sur- re- - xit
Et re- sur- re- xit ter-
-pul- tus est, pas- - sus, et se- pul- tus est.
est, pas- - sus, et se- pul- tus est. Et re- sur- re- xit
Et re- sur- re- - xit ter-
4 [♮]3 6 7 6

75
ter- ti- a di- e, se- cun- dum Scri- ptu- - ras.
- ti- a di- e, se- cun- dum Scri- ptu- - ras.
-ti- a di- - e, se- cun- dum Scri- ptu- - ras.
4 3 6 4 [♮]3
80
se- det ad
Et a- scen- dit in cae- lum, in cae- lum:
Et a- scen- dit in cae- lum: se- det ad
a- scen- dit in cae- - lum
a- scen- dit in cae- lum: se-
[6]

85
de- xte- ram Pa- - tris. Et i- te- rum ven-
se- det ad de- xte-ram Pa- - tris.
de- xte- ram Pa- - tris. Et i- te- rum ven-
Et i- te- rum
-det ad de- xte- ram Pa- tris. Et i- te- rum ven- tu- rus
4 3 6 5
90
-tu- rus est cum glo- - - ri- a,
cum glo- ri- a, cum glo-
-tu- rus est cum glo- - ri- a,
cum glo- - ri- a, cum glo- ri-
est cum glo- - ri- a, cum glo-
4 3

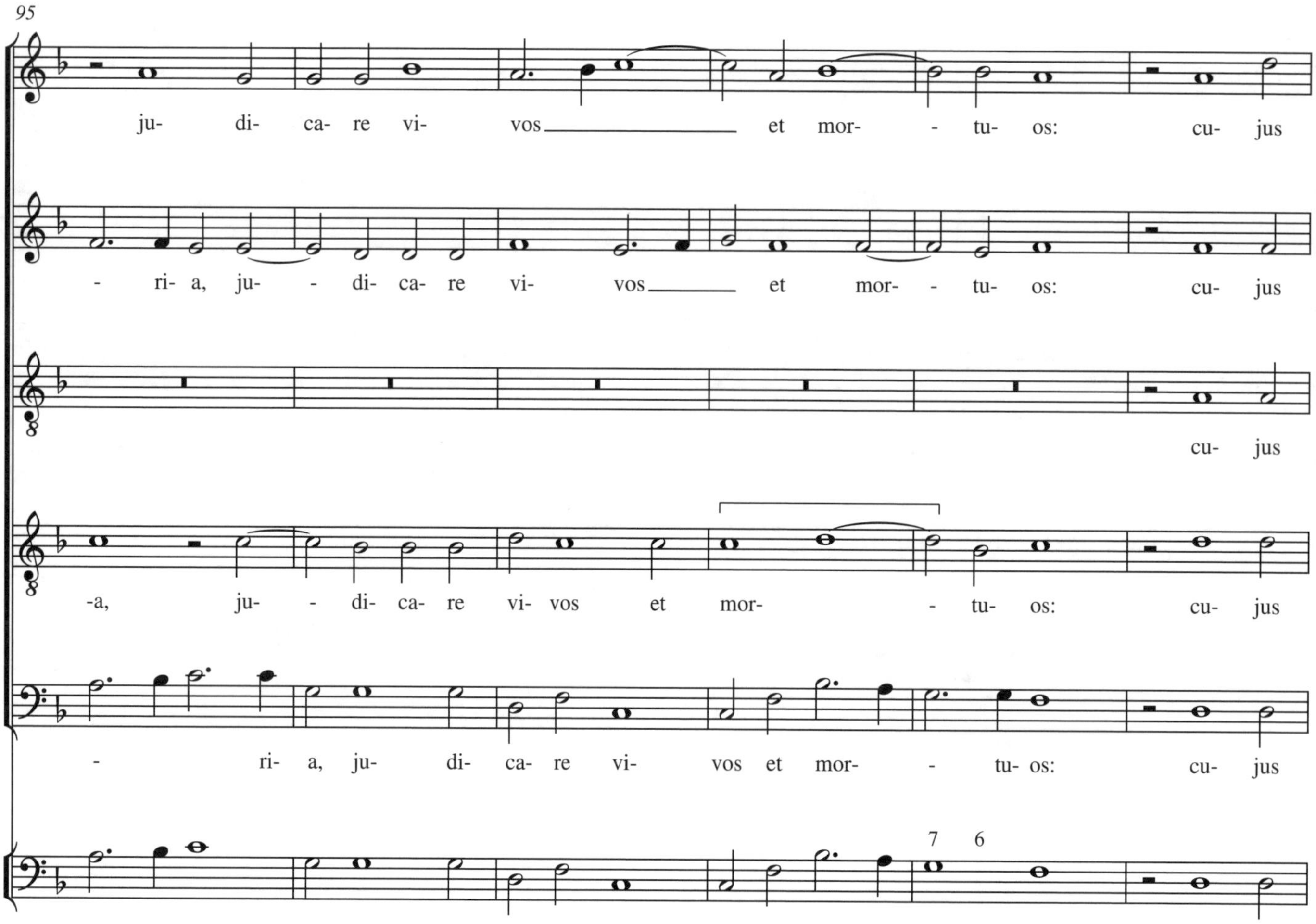
95
ju- di- ca- re vi- vos et mor- - tu- os: cu- jus
- ri- a, ju- - di- ca- re vi- vos et mor- - tu- os: cu- jus
cu- jus
-a, ju- - di- ca- re vi- vos et mor- - tu- os: cu- jus
- ri- a, ju- di- ca- re vi- vos et mor- - tu- os: cu- jus
7 6

101
re- gni non e- rit fi- nis, non e- rit fi- nis.
re- gni non e- rit, non e- rit fi- nis, non e- rit fi- nis.
re- gni non e- rit, non e- rit fi- nis, non e- rit fi- nis.
re- gni non e- rit fi- - nis, non e- rit fi- nis.
re- gni non e- - rit fi- nis, non e- rit fi- nis.
♯

106
Et in Spi- ri- tum San- ctum, Do- mi- num, et vi- vi- fi-
Et in Spi- ri- tum San- ctum, Do- mi- num, et vi- vi-
Et in Spi- ri- tum San- ctum, Do- mi- num, et vi- vi- fi-
Et in Spi- ri- tum San- ctum, Do- mi- num, et vi-
111
et Fi-
-can- tem Qui cum Pa- tre et
- fi- can- tem Qui cum Pa- tre et
-can- tem: qui ex Pa- tre Fi- li- o- que pro- ce- - dit. et
-vi- fi- can- tem: qui ex Pa- tre Fi- li- o- que pro- ce- dit.
4 3

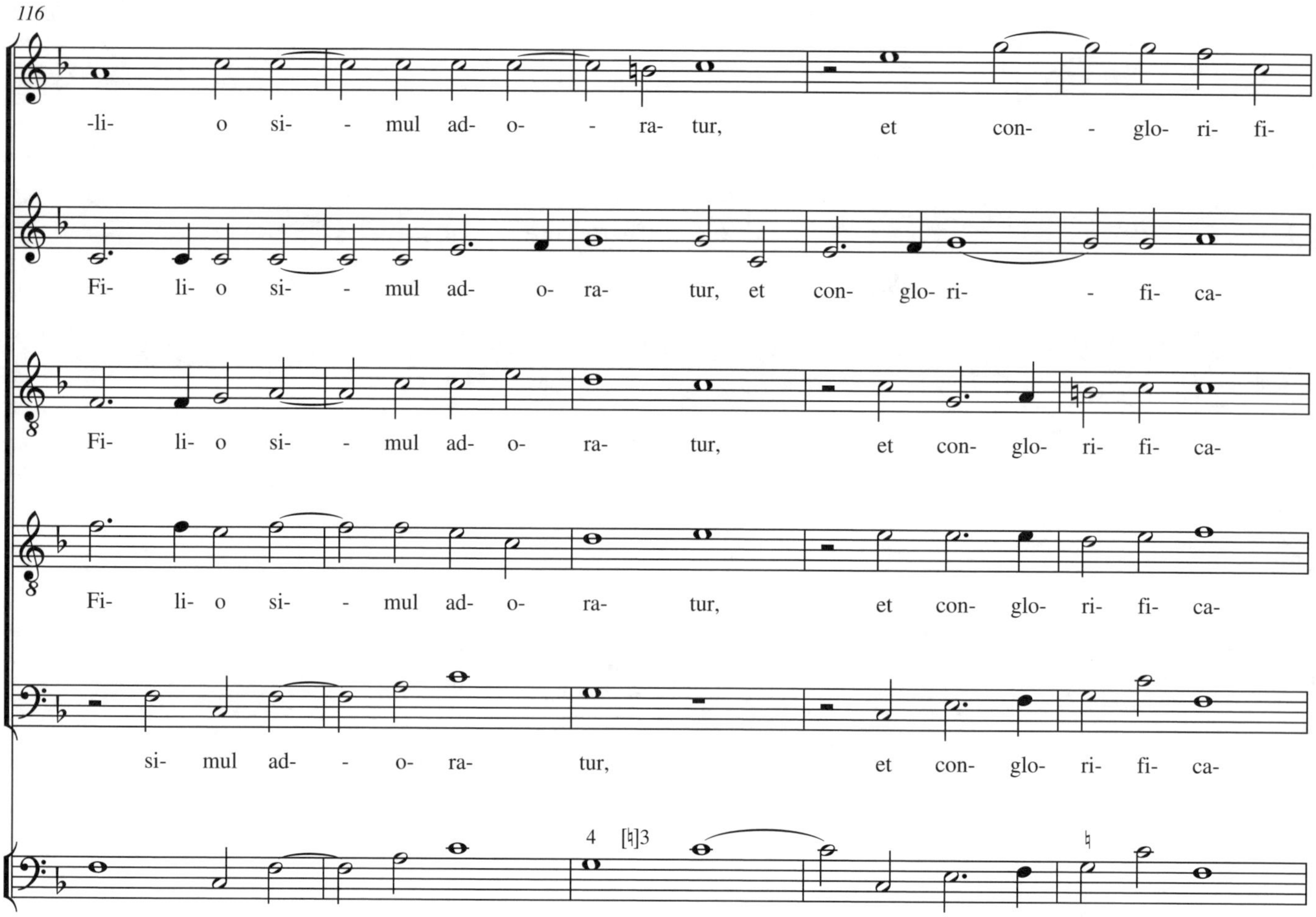
116
-li- o si- - mul ad- o- - ra- tur, et con- - glo- ri- fi-
Fi- li- o si- - mul ad- o- ra- tur, et con- glo- ri- - fi- ca-
Fi- li- o si- - mul ad- o- ra- tur, et con- glo- ri- fi- ca-
Fi- li- o si- - mul ad- o- ra- tur, et con- glo- ri- fi- ca-
si- mul ad- - o- ra- tur, et con- glo- ri- fi- ca-
4 [♮]3
♮

121
-ca- tur: qui lo- cu- tus est per Pro- phe- tas. Et u- nam san-
-tur: qui lo- cu- tus est per Pro- phe- tas. Et u- nam san-
-tur: qui lo- cu- tus est per Pro- phe- - tas.
-tur: qui lo- cu- tus est per Pro- phe- - tas.
-tur: qui lo- cu- tus est per Pro- phe- - tas.
4 [♮]3 6
4 3
[6] 6

126
-ctam Con- fi-
-ctam Con-
san- ctam ca- tho- li- cam et a- po- sto- li- cam Ec- cle- - si- am.
san- ctam ca- tho- li- cam et a- po- sto- li- cam Ec- cle- si- am.
et a- po- sto- li- cam Ec- cle- si- am. Con-
4 [♮]3
131
- - te- or in re- mis- si- o-
-fi- - te- or u- num ba- pti- sma in re- mis- si- o- nem
u- num ba- pti- - sma
u- num ba- pti- - sma in re- mis- si-
-fi- - te- or in re- mis- si-
5 6 5 6 4 3

136
-nem pec- ca- - to- rum.
pec- ca- to- rum. re- - sur- re- cti- o- nem mor- tu-
Et ex- spe- cto re- sur- re- cti- o- nem
-o- nem pec- ca- to- rum. Et ex- spe- cto
-o- nem pec- ca- to- rum. Et ex- spe- cto
4 [♯]3 4 [♯]3
141
Et vi- - tam ven- tu- ri sae- cu- li.
-o- rum.
mor- tu- o- rum. Et vi- tam ven- tu- ri sae- cu- li. A-
Et vi- tam ven- tu- ri sae- - cu- li. A- men,
Et vi- tam ven- tu- - ri sae- cu- li. A-
6 ♮ 6 4 [♮]3 7 6

171

Sanctus

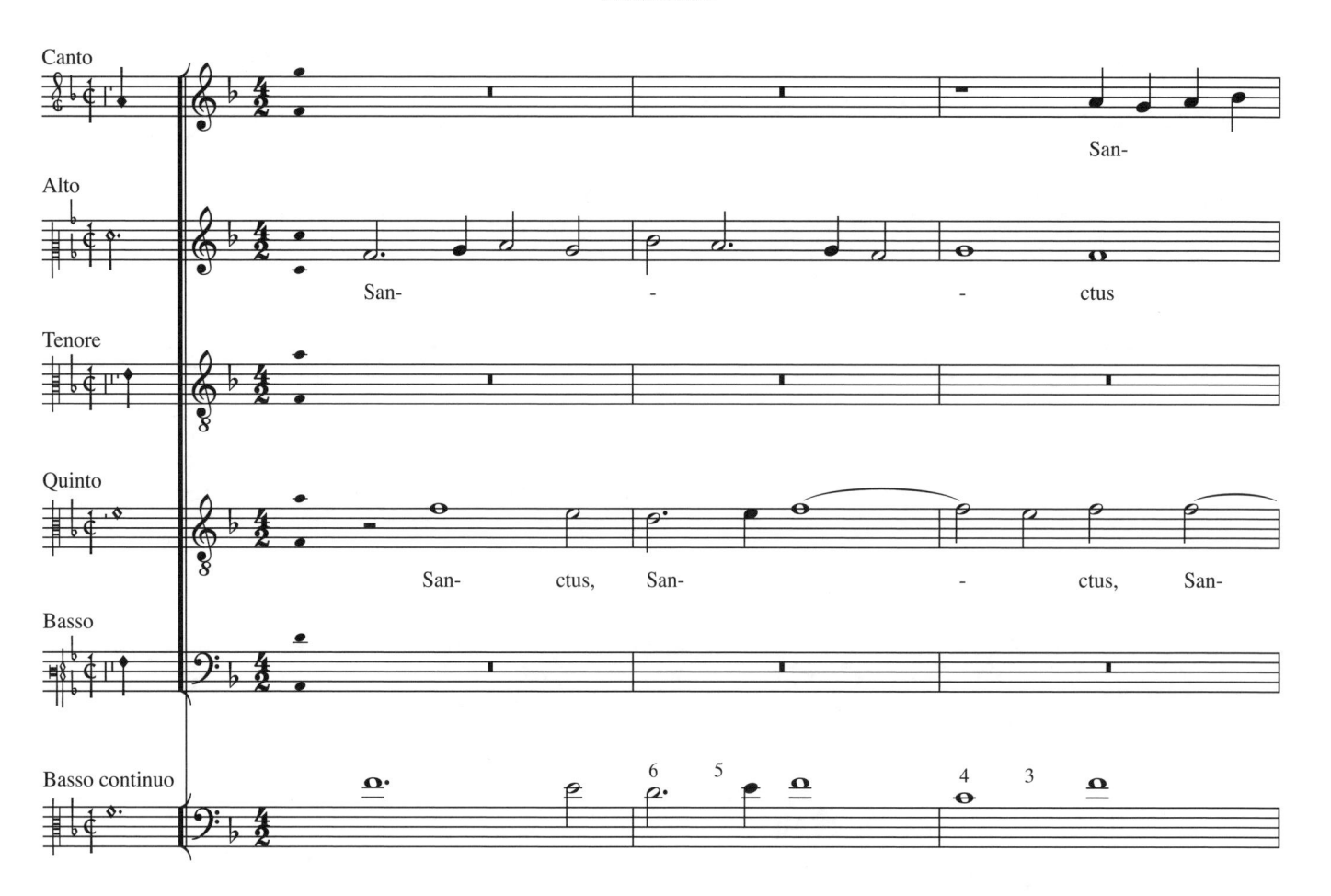

4
- - - - ctus
Do- mi- nus
San- - - ctus
- ctus, San- - ctus Do-
San- - - ctus Do- mi- nus
6 5 4 [♮]3
8
Do- mi-nus De- us Sa- - ba- oth.
De- us Sa- - ba- oth, Do- mi-nus De- us Sa- ba-
Do- - mi-nus De- us Sa- ba- oth. Ple-
- mi-nus De- us Sa- ba-oth, Do- - mi-nus De- us Sa- ba- oth.
De- us Sa- ba- oth, Do- mi- nus De- us Sa- ba- oth. Ple-

13
-oth. Ple- - ni sunt cae- - - li
- ni sunt cae- - li et ter- -
- ni sunt cae- - li et ter- -
6 5
17
glo- ri- a tu- -
- ra glo- ri- a tu- - a.
glo- ri- a tu-
- ra glo- ri- a tu- - a.
4 [♮]3

21
- a. Ho- san- na
Ho- san- na in ex- cel- -
Ho- san- na in ex- cel- - -
- a.
Ho- san- na in ex- cel- - -
6
26
in ex- cel- sis, ho- san- na in ex- - cel- sis,
- - sis, ho- san-
- - sis, ho-
Ho- san- - na in ex- cel- sis,
- - sis, ho- san- na in ex- cel- sis, ho-
7 6 7 6 6 4 3 7 ♮6 4 [♮]3

31
hosan- - - na
- - na, hosan- na in ex- cel-
-san- - na in ex- cel- sis, ho- san-
ho- san- na in ex-
-san- na, ho- san- na in ex- cel-
5 6 4 3
35
in ex- cel- sis. Be- ne- di- ctus qui ve-
-sis, in ex- cel- sis. Be- ne-
-na in ex- cel- sis.
-cel- - sis.
- - sis. Be- ne- di- ctus qui ve-

-nit, qui ve- - nit,

-di- ctus qui ve- -

Be- ne- di- - ctus qui ve-

Be- ne- di- - ctus qui

-nit

be- - ne- di- ctus qui ve-

-nit in no- mi- ne Do- mi- ni,

-nit in no- mi- ne Do- mi- ni.

ve- nit in no- mi- ne Do- mi- ni, in no- mi- ne Do-

in no- mi- ne Do- mi- ni, in no- - mi- ne

49
- nit in no- mi- ne Do- - mi- ni.
in no- mi- ne Do- - mi- ni. Ho- san- na
Ho- san- na in ex- cel-
-mi- ni, in no- mi- ne Do- - mi- ni.
Do- mi- ni, in no- mi- ne Do- mi- ni. Ho- san- na in ex- cel-
4 [♮]3 2 4 3 6
54
Ho- san- na in ex- cel- sis, ho-
in ex- cel- - - - sis,
- - - - sis,
Ho- san-
- - - - sis, ho- san-
7 6 7 6 6 4 3

59
-san- na in ex- - cel- sis, ho- san-
ho- san- - - na,
ho- san- - na in ex-
- na in ex- cel- sis, ho-
-na in ex- cel- sis, ho- san- na, ho- san-
7 ♮6 4 [♮]3
63
- - na in ex- cel- sis.
ho- san- na in ex- cel- sis, in ex- cel- sis.
-cel- sis, ho- san- na in ex- cel- sis.
-san- na in ex- cel- - sis.
-na in ex- cel- - - sis.
5 6 4 3

Agnus Dei

181

20
no- bis, mi- se- re- re no-
- bis, mi- se- re- re no- -
-re- re no- bis,
mi- - se- re- - re no- -
no- bis, mi- se- re- re no- -
6 4 3 ♮
24
- bis, mi- se- re- re no- bis.
- bis, mi- - se- re- - re no- bis.
mi- se- re- re no- bis.
- - bis, mi- - se- re- re no- bis.
- bis, mi- se- re- re no- bis.
4 3

Masses from
*Messe et Magnificat
a quattro voci,* Op. 19

Dedication

ILLUSTRISS. ET ECCELENTISS.
Signore Patron Collendissimo.

L'essibire queste compositioni all'occhio sublime dell'E[cellenza] V[ostra] è un desiderio di far conoscer più i testimonij della mia antica, divota osservanza, che i tratti musici della mia penna. La brama di presentarle rinovata la mia servitù, m'eccitò in allegra opportunità à proporgliela distesa in canto sù questi fogli. Seguitai per lungo tempo, se ben distante di persona, certo in vicinanza d'animo, e di riverenza i giri dell'E. V. L'osservai scorrer per tant'anni a gran passi di gloria la nostra Europa nelle Publiche Legazioni occupando in amore i cuori de'più gran Prencipi. Le giuro, che sino in aspetto dell'Asia mi sono trovato seco; e sù l'ali de gl'assetti mi sono portato sino in Bisanzio à rendermi ammiratore de'suoi maneggi, verso i quali fatta dolcemente ossequiosa, conobbi, che non seppe d'haver sensi barbari la Ferità. Ora che l'E. V. scorta da quel raggio, ch'è guida à gl'Eroi felicemente ritornò in patria, seco lasciò di peregrinar il mio cuore. Il quale, se per lei assente offerì al Signor Dio mille voti, à lei presente in testimonio del proprio allegro riposo ardisce tributar questi fogli. Supplico l'E. V. sù queste note di canto conoscere i contrasegni d'un suo umilissimo servitor; il quale teneva giusto diritto di dover muovere la propria arte ad osequiare co'suoi co[n]certi, chi viene riverito per l'anima armonica di questo Publico, e ad inchinare con le sue misure chi tiene la perfezione de'più gran numeri. Il nome dell'E. V., solito ad essere inciso su la tromba d'oro della Fama, ardisco di far leggere scritto in fronte à quest'opera. E lo fò per vantaggio di queste mie compositioni, onde partecipino l'onore del titolo, che le contrasegna; cosi un raggio sul petto ad un vapore il qualifica con aspetto di stella, e riverire lo fà sotto Imagine di miracolo. Perdoni dunque l'E. V. la fiacchezza di quest'offerta, e l'usurpazione del suo gran Nome. Questo si dirà benignamente concesso; quella si confesserà incautamente praticata, da chi ciecamente rapito dal vigore del proprio ossequio, s'inchina.

Di V. E.
Humiliss. Devotiss. & Obligatiss. Servitore
D[OMINO] NATALE MONFERRATO.

My Most Illustrious and Most Excellent Lord and Most Respected Master,

To submit these compositions to the sublime gaze of Your Excellency arises from a wish to broadcast the evidence of my long-standing, devout respect [for you] rather than the musical strokes of my pen. The desire to renew my service to you afforded me the joyful opportunity to express this in the form of the vocal works on these pages. For a long time I followed, though distantly in space, certainly closely in spirit and regard, Your Excellency's travels. I saw you for so many years gloriously bestride our Europe in public legations, capturing the affections of the greatest princes. I swear that I was with you to the very gates of Asia, and that on a flying carpet I was carried as far as Byzantium [Istanbul] so as to be able to admire your dealings, towards which, as I learned, having been made sweetly respectful, cruelty itself was unable to harbor barbarous feelings. Now that Your Excellency, escorted by that ray of light which is a guide to heroes, has happily returned home, my heart has ceased to wander. Which heart, though it offered to the Lord God a thousand prayers for you in your absence, now, in your presence, ventures to offer you these pages in testimony of its own happy repose. I beg Your Excellency to recognize in these musical notes the mark of a most humble servant, who has thought it right to use his own art to pay tribute through his compositions to a person who is revered by the harmonious soul of this public and with his musical measures to bow before a person who possesses the perfection of the greatest numbers. I make so bold as to print Your Excellency's name, accustomed to being engraved on the golden trumpet of fame, at the head of this work. And I do this for the advantage of these compositions of mine, so that they may share the honor of the title that I attach to them, in the same way as a ray of light falling on a vapor lends it the aspect of a star and causes it to be worshipped as a miracle. May Your Excellency therefore forgive the feebleness of this offering and the usurpation of your great name. The latter will be said to be graciously granted; the former will be admitted to be incautiously attempted by a person who, blindly carried away by the force of his own devotion, bows before you.

Your Excellency's most humble, devout, and obliging servant,
Lord Natale Monferrato.

Translation by Michael Talbot

Messa a cappella

Kyrie

15
Ky- ri- e e- le- i- son, e- le-
Ky- ri- e e- le- - i- son, e-
-e e- le- i- son, Ky- ri- e, Ky- ri- e e-
e- le- i- son, Ky- ri- e, Ky- ri- e e-
20
- i- son. Chri- ste e- le- i- son,
-le- i- son. Chri- ste e- le- i- son, e- le- -
-le- i- son. Chri- ste e- le- i- son, e- le- - i- son,
-le- i- son. Chri- ste e- le- i- son,
26
Chri- ste, Chri- ste e- le- i- son, e- le-
- i- son, Chri- ste e- le- - i- son, e- le-
e- le- - i- son, Chri- ste e- le- i- son, e- le-
e- le- i- son, Chri- ste e- le- i- son, e- le-

187

47
-son,
Ky- ri- e e- le- - - i-
-son, e- le- i- son, Ky- ri- e e- le- i-
-son, Ky- ri- e e- le- - i-
52
Ky- ri- e e- le- i- son, e- le- i- son, e-
-son, Ky- - ri- e e- le- i- son, Ky- ri- e e- le- - i- son,
-son, Ky- ri- e e- le- i- son, Ky- ri- e e- le- i- son,
-son, Ky- - ri- e e- le- i- son, Ky- ri- e e-
58
-le- - i- son, Ky- ri- e e- le- i- son, Ky-
Ky- - ri- e e- le- i-
Ky- - ri- e e- le- i- son,
-le- - i- son, Ky- ri- e e- le- i- son,

Gloria

10
- mus. Ad- o- ra- mus te. Glo- ri- fi-
- mus. Ad- o- ra- mus te. Glo- ri- fi-
-da- mus. Be- - ne- di- - ci- mus te. Glo- ri- fi- ca- mus
Be- - ne- di- ci- mus te. Ad- o- ra- mus te.
15
-ca- mus te, glo- ri- fi- ca- - mus te. Gra- ti-
-ca- mus te, glo- ri- fi- ca- mus te. Gra- ti-
te, glo- ri- fi- ca- mus te, glo- ri- fi- ca- mus te. Gra-
Glo- ri- fi- ca- mus te, glo- ri- fi- ca- mus te.
20
-as a- gi- mus ti- - bi pro-
-as a- gi- mus ti- - bi
- ti- as a- gi- mus ti- - bi pro- pter ma- gnam glo- ri-
pro- pter ma- gnam glo- ri-

25
- pter ma- gnam glo- ri- am tu- am.
Do- mi- ne De- us, Rex cae- le-
-am tu- - am, glo- - ri- am tu- am.
-am, glo- ri- am tu- - am. Do- mi- ne De- us, Rex cae-
30
Do- mi- ne Fi- li u- ni- ge- ni-
- stis, De- us Pa- ter om- ni- po- tens. Do- mi- ne
-le- stis, De- - us Pa- ter om- ni- po- tens. Do- mi- ne Fi- li u- ni-
36
-te Je- su Chri- ste. A-
Fi- li u- ni- ge- ni- te Je- su Chri- - ste. A-
Do- mi- ne De-
-ge- ni- te Je- su Chri- ste. Do- mi- - ne De-

41
- gnus De- i, Fi- li- us Pa- tris.
- gnus De- i, Fi- li- us Pa- -
-us, Fi- li- us Pa- - -
- us, Fi- li- us Pa- -
45
Qui tol- - lis pec- ca- ta mun- di, pec- ca-
- tris. Qui tol- lis pec- ca- ta
- tris. Qui tol- lis pec- ca- ta mun- - di, pec- ca- ta mun-
- tris. Qui tol- lis pec- ca- ta mun- di, pec- ca-
50
-ta mun- di, mi- se- re- re no- - bis.
mun- di Qui tol- -
- - di, mi- se- re- re no- bis. Qui tol-
-ta mun- di, mi- se- re- re no- - bis. Qui tol-

-lis pec- ca- ta mun- di,
-lis pec- ca- ta mun- di,
-lis pec- ca- ta mun- di,

su- sci- pe de- pre- ca- ti- o- nem no- stram. Qui
su- sci- pe de- pre- ca- ti- o- nem no- stram. Qui se-
su- sci- pe de- pre- ca- ti- o- nem no- stram. Qui
su- sci- pe

se- des ad de- xte- ram Pa-
-des ad de- xte- ram Pa-
se- des ad de- xte- ram Pa- tris,
ad de- xte- ram Pa- tris,

70
-tris, mi- se- re- re no- bis.
-tris, mi- se- re- re no- - - -
mi- se- re- re no- bis, mi- se- re- re no- - -
mi- se- re- - re no- bis, mi- se- re- re no- bis, mi- se- re- re no-
76
Quo- ni- am tu so- lus Tu so- lus Do- mi- nus. Tu so-
-bis. tu so- lus san- ctus. Tu so- lus Do- mi- nus. Tu
-bis. Quo- ni- am tu so- lus Tu
-bis. tu so- lus san- ctus. Tu so-
81
- lus Al- tis- si- mus, Je- - su Chri- ste.
so- lus Al- tis- si- mus, Je- - su Chri- ste. Cum San- cto
so- lus Al- tis- si- mus, Je- su, ⟨Je- - su⟩ Chri- ste.
- lus Al- tis- si- mus, Je- su Chri- ste. Cum San- cto

86
Cum Sancto Spi- ri- tu, De- i Pa- tris. A-
Spi- - ri- tu, De- i Pa- tris. A-
in glo- ri- a De- i Pa- tris. A-
Spi- - ri- tu, in glo- ri- a
91
-men, a- - men, ⟨a- - men,⟩
- men, a- - men, ⟨a-
- men, a- - men, a-
A- - men, a- - men,
95
a- - men, a- men, a- men.
- men,⟩ a- men, a- men, a- men.
- men, a- men, a- men, a- men.
a- - men, a- men, a- men.

Credo

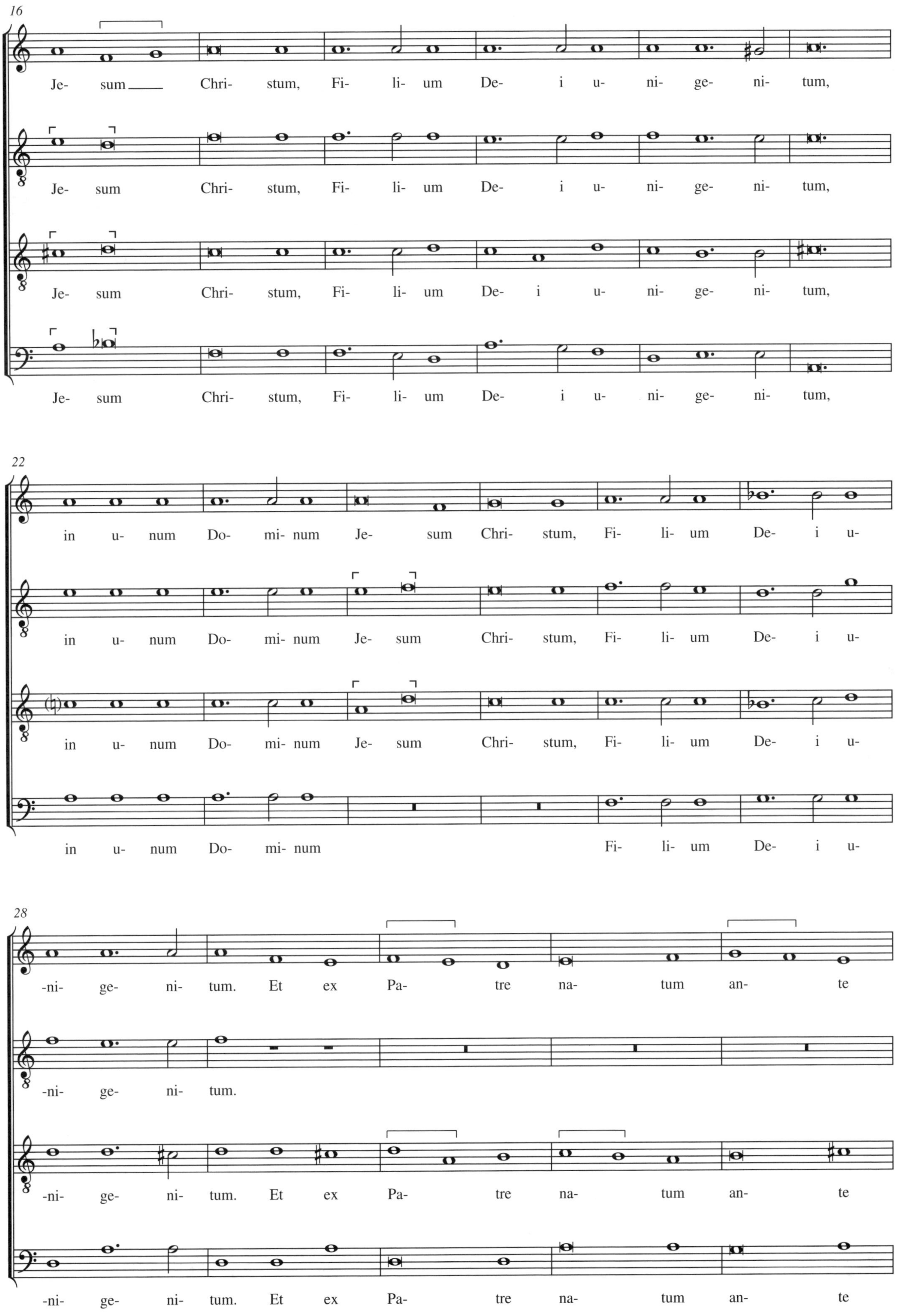
16
Je- sum Chri- stum, Fi- li- um De- i u- ni- ge- ni- tum,
Je- sum Chri- stum, Fi- li- um De- i u- ni- ge- ni- tum,
Je- sum Chri- stum, Fi- li- um De- i u- ni- ge- ni- tum,
Je- sum Chri- stum, Fi- li- um De- i u- ni- ge- ni- tum,
22
in u- num Do- mi- num Je- sum Chri- stum, Fi- li- um De- i u-
in u- num Do- mi- num Je- sum Chri- stum, Fi- li- um De- i u-
in u- num Do- mi- num Je- sum Chri- stum, Fi- li- um De- i u-
in u- num Do- mi- num Fi- li- um De- i u-
28
-ni- ge- ni- tum. Et ex Pa- tre na- tum an- te
-ni- ge- ni- tum.
-ni- ge- ni- tum. Et ex Pa- tre na- tum an- te
-ni- ge- ni- tum. Et ex Pa- tre na- tum an- te

33
om- ni- a sae- cu- la. De- um de De- o,
De- um de De- - o,
om- ni- a sae- cu- la. lu- men de
om- ni- a sae- cu- la. De- um de De-
38
lu- men de lu- mi- ne
lu- men de lu- mi- ne, De- um ve- - rum de
lu- mi- ne, De- um ve- - - rum de
- o, De- um ve- - rum de
43
Ge- ni- tum, non fa- ctum,
De- o ve- ro. Ge- ni- tum, non fa- ctum,
De- o ve- ro. Ge- ni- tum, non fa- ctum,
De- o ve- ro. Ge- ni- tum, non fa- ctum,

48
con- sub- stan- ti- a- lem Pa- tri: per quem om- ni- a fa- cta sunt.
con- sub- stan- ti- a- lem Pa- tri: per quem om- ni- a fa- cta sunt.
con- sub- stan- ti- a- lem Pa- tri: per quem om- ni- a fa- cta sunt.
con- sub- stan- ti- a- lem Pa- tri: per quem om- ni- a fa- cta sunt.
54
Ge- ni- tum, non fa- ctum, con- sub- stan- ti- a- lem Pa- tri: per quem
Ge- ni- tum, non fa- ctum, con- sub- stan- ti- a- lem Pa- tri: per quem
Ge- ni- tum, non fa- ctum, con- sub- stan- ti- a- lem Pa- tri: per quem
Ge- ni- tum, non fa- ctum, con- sub- stan- ti- a- lem Pa- tri: per quem
59
om- ni- a fa- cta sunt. Qui pro- pter nos ho- mi- nes,
om- ni- a fa- cta sunt.
om- ni- a fa- cta sunt. Qui pro- pter nos ho- mi- nes,
om- ni- a fa- cta sunt. Qui pro- pter nos ho- mi-

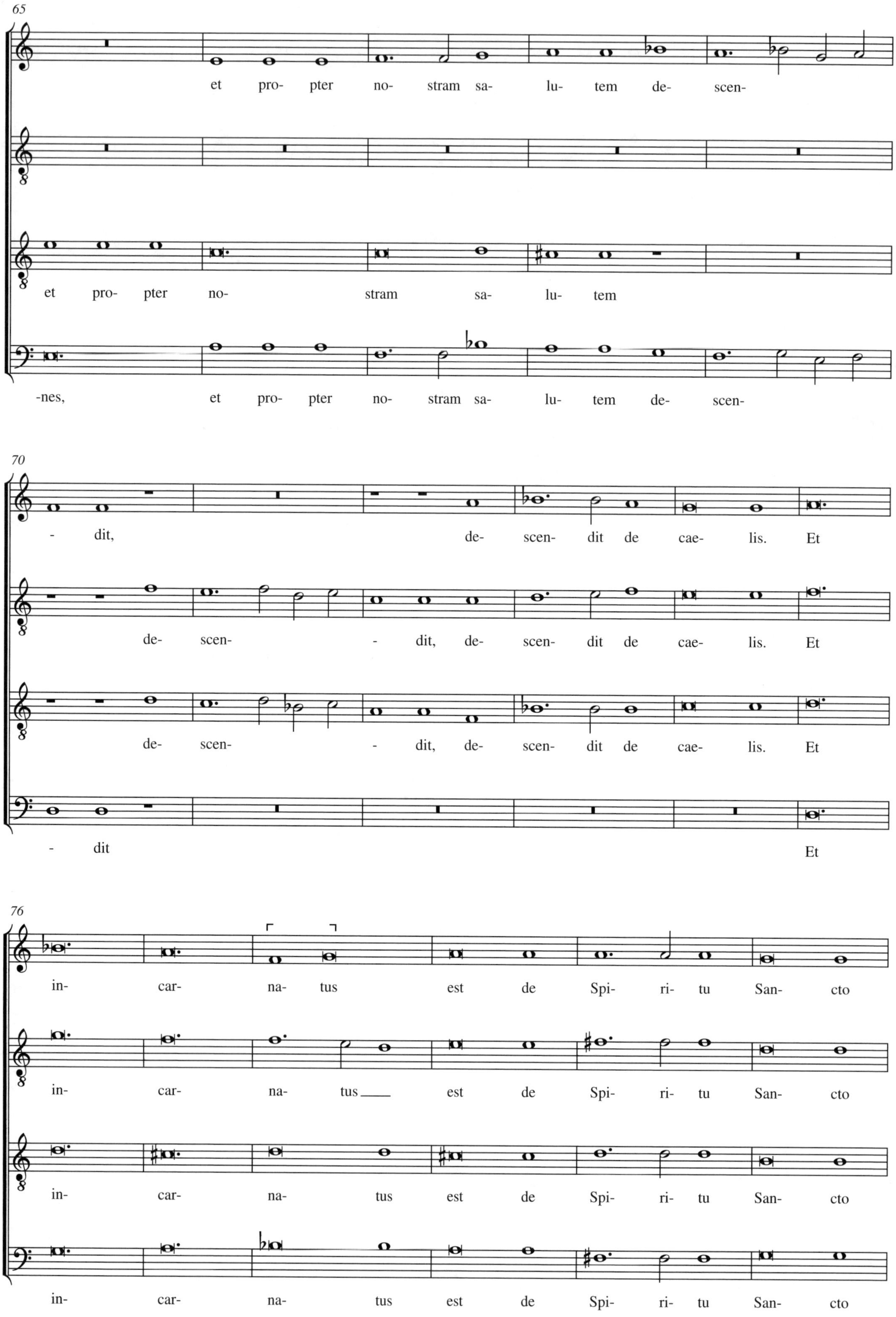
65
et pro- pter no- stram sa- lu- tem de- scen-
et pro- pter no- stram sa- lu- tem
-nes, et pro- pter no- stram sa- lu- tem de- scen-
70
- dit, de- scen- dit de cae- lis. Et
de- scen- - dit, de- scen- dit de cae- lis. Et
de- scen- - dit, de- scen- dit de cae- lis. Et
- dit Et
76
in- car- na- tus est de Spi- ri- tu San- cto
in- car- na- tus est de Spi- ri- tu San- cto
in- car- na- tus est de Spi- ri- tu San- cto
in- car- na- tus est de Spi- ri- tu San- cto

ex Maria Virgine: et homo factus est, et
ex Maria Virgine: et homo factus est, et
ex Maria Virgine: et homo factus est, et
ex Maria Virgine: et homo factus est, et

homo factus est. sub
homo factus est.
homo factus est. Crucifixus etiam pro no-
homo factus est. Crucifixus etiam pro no-

Pontio Pilato passus, et sepultus est.
Et resurre-
-bis: sub Pontio Pilato passus, et sepultus est. Et resurre-
-bis: passus, et sepultus est. Et resurre-

99
-xit ter- - ti- a di- - e, se- cun- dum Scri- ptu-
-xit ter- ti- a di- - e, se- cun- dum Scri- ptu-
-xit ter- ti- a di- - e, se- cun- dum Scri- ptu- ras.
104
Et a- scen- dit in cae- - lum
-ras. Et a- scen- dit in cae- lum
-ras. se- det ad de- xte-ram Pa- -
Et a- scen- - dit in cae- lum: se- det ad de- xte- ram Pa-
109
Et i- te- rum ven- tu- rus est cum glo- ri- a, ju-
Et i- te- rum ven- tu- rus est cum glo- - ri- a,
- tris. Et i- te- rum ven- tu- rus est cum glo- ri- a,
- tris. Et i- te- rum ju- di-

114
- di- ca- re vi- vos cu- jus re-
et mor- tu- os: cu- jus re-
ju- di- ca- re vi- vos et mor- tu- os: cu- jus
-ca- re vi- vos et mor- tu- os: cu- jus re-
119
-gni non e- - rit fi- nis. Et in Spi- ri- tum San-
-gni Et in Spi- ri- tum San-
re- gni non e- rit fi- nis. Et in Spi- ri- tum San-
-gni non e- rit, non e- rit fi- nis. Et in Spi- ri- tum San-
124
- ctum, Do- - mi- num, et vi- vi- fi- can- - tem
- ctum, Do- - mi- num, et vi- vi- fi- can- - tem
- ctum, Do- - mi- num, et vi- vi- fi- can- - tem: qui
- ctum, Do- - mi- num, et vi- vi- fi- can- - tem:

130
Qui cum
Qui
ex Pa- - tre Fi- - li- o- que pro- ce- dit. Qui
qui ex Pa- - tre Fi- - li- o- que pro- ce- dit.
135
Pa- - tre et Fi- li- o si- - mul ad- o- ra- tur,
cum Pa- - tre et Fi- li- o si- - mul ad- o- ra-
cum Pa- tre et Fi- li- o si- - mul ad- o- ra-
si- mul ad- o- ra- -
140
et con- glo- ri- fi- ca- tur: qui lo- cu-
- tur, et con- glo- ri- fi- ca- - tur: qui lo-
- tur, et con- glo- ri- fi- ca- - tur: qui lo-
-tur, et con- glo- ri- fi- ca- - tur: qui lo-

145
-tus est per Pro- phe- tas. Et u- nam san-
-cu- tus est per Pro- phe- - tas. Et u- nam,
-cu- tus est per Pro-phe- tas. Et u- nam san- ctam ca-
-cu- tus est Et u- nam
150
-ctam ca- tho- li- cam, ⟨et u- nam san- ctam ca- tho- li- cam⟩
et u- nam san- ctam ca- tho- li- cam et a- po- sto- li-
-tho- li- cam, et u- nam san- ctam ca- tho- li- cam et a-
et a- po- sto-
155
Con- fi- te- or u- num ba- pti- sma in re-
-cam Ec- cle- - si- am. Con- fi- te- or u- num ba- - pti- sma
- po- sto- li- cam Ec- cle- si- am. u- num ba- pti- sma in re-mis- si-
-li- cam Ec- cle- si- am.

161
-mis- si- o- nem pec- ca- to- rum. re- sur- re- cti- o-
Et ex- spe- - cto re- - sur- re- cti-
-o- nem pec- - ca- to- rum. Et ex- spe- cto re- - sur- re- cti-
pec- ca- to- rum. Et ex- spe- cto
166
- nem mor- tu- - o- rum.
-o- nem mor- tu- o- rum. Et vi- tam ven- tu- ri sae- cu-
-o- nem mor- tu- o- rum. Et vi- tam ven- tu- ri sae- cu-
Et vi- tam ven- tu- ri sae- cu- li.
171
A- - - - - men,
-li, ven- tu- ri
-li. A- - - - - men.
A- - - men. ven- tu- ri

Sanctus

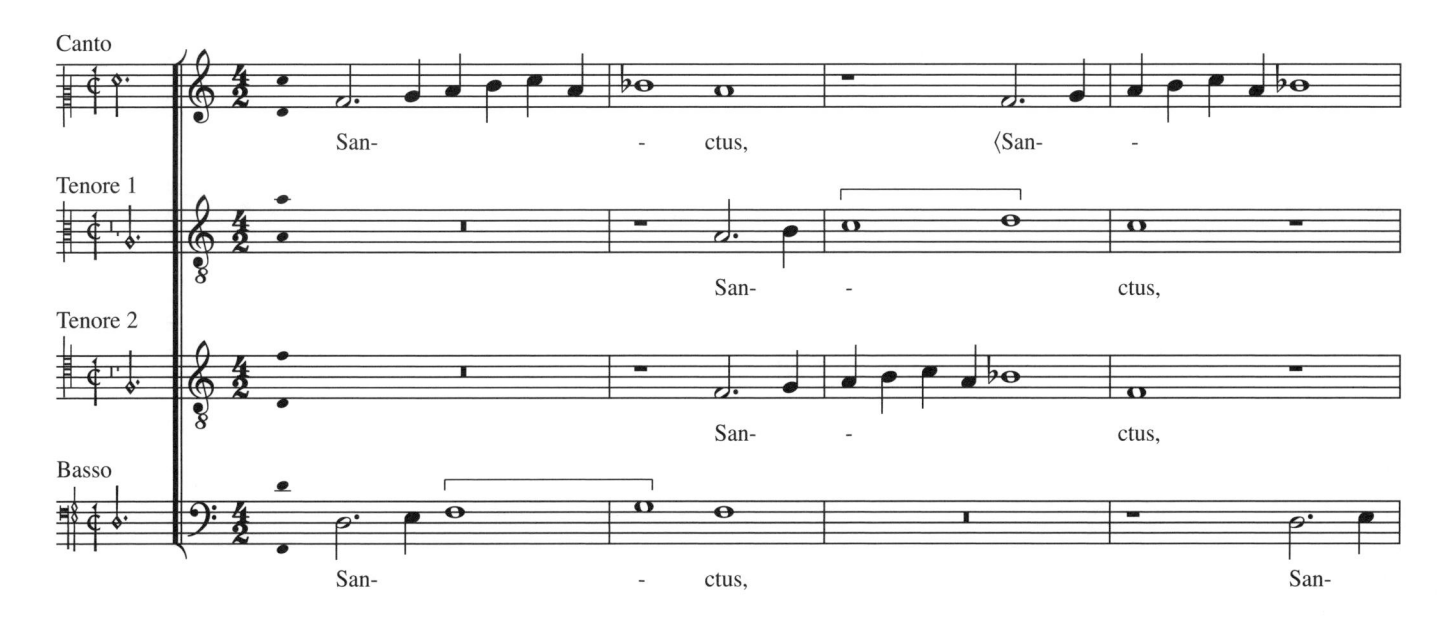

5
-ctus⟩ Do-
San- - - - - ctus
San- ctus, ⟨San- ctus,⟩ San- - - ctus
- ctus, San- - - ctus Do-
10
-mi- nus De- us Sa- ba- oth. Ple- ni
Do- mi- nus De- us Sa- ba- oth.
Do- mi- nus De- us Sa- ba- oth. Ple- - ni
-mi- nus De- us Sa- ba- oth, Do- mi- nus De- us Sa- ba- oth. Ple- ni
15
sunt cae- li et ter- ra glo- ri- a tu- a. Ho- san- na
cae- li et ter- ra Ho-
sunt cae- li et ter- ra glo- - ri- a, glo- ri- a tu- a. Ho- san- na
sunt cae- li et ter- ra glo- ri- a, glo- ri- a tu- a. Ho-

20
in ex- cel- sis, ho- san- - na in ex- cel- -
-san- na in ex- cel- sis, ho- san- - na in ex- cel- -
in ex- cel- sis, ho- san- - na in ex- cel- - sis, ho-
-san- na in ex- cel- sis, ho- san- na in ex- cel- - sis,
25
-sis, ho- san- - na in ex- cel- sis.
-sis, ho- san- - na in ex- cel- - sis.
- san- - na in ex- cel- - sis.
ho- san- na, ho- san- na in ex- cel- sis.
31
Be- ne- di- ctus qui ve- - -
Be- ne- di- ctus qui ve- - -
Be- ne- di- ctus qui ve- - -

36
Ho- san-
- nit in no- mi- ne, in no- mi- ne Do- mi- ni. Ho-
- nit in no- mi- ne, in no- mi- ne Do- mi- ni. Ho-
- nit in no- mi- ne, in no- mi- ne Do- mi- ni. Ho- san- na
41
- na in ex- cel- - sis,
- san- na in ex- cel- - sis, ho- san-
-san- na in ex- cel- - sis, ho- - san-
in ex- cel- - - sis, ho- san-
45
ho- san- - na in ex- cel- sis.
- na in ex- cel- - sis.
- na in ex- cel- - sis.
-na, ho- san- na in ex- cel- sis.

Agnus Dei

13
no- - bis, mi- se- re- re no-
mi- - se- re- - re no-
mi- se- re- re no- bis, mi-
-re- re no- - bis,
18
- - bis, mi- se- re-
- - bis, mi- se- re- - re no-
- se- re- re no- bis, mi- - se- re-
mi- - se- re- re,
22
- re, mi- - se- re- - re no- bis.
- bis, mi- - se- re- - re no- bis.
-re, mi- - se- re- - re no- bis.
mi- - se- re- - re no- bis.

Messa breve

Kyrie

15
— e- le- i- son, Chri- ste e- le- i- son, e- le- i-
- i- son, Chri- ste e- le- i- son, Chri- ste e- le- i-
Chri- ste e- le- i- son, Chri- ste e- le- i- son, e-
-le- i- son, Chri- ste e- le- i- son, Chri- ste
20
-son, e- le- i- son. Ky- ri- e e- le- i- son,
-son, e- le- - i- son. Ky- ri- e e- le- i- son, e-
-le- - i- son.
e- le- - i- son.
25
e- le- - i- son,
-le- - i- son,
Ky- ri- e e- le- i- son, e- le-
Ky- ri- e e- le- i- son, e- le-

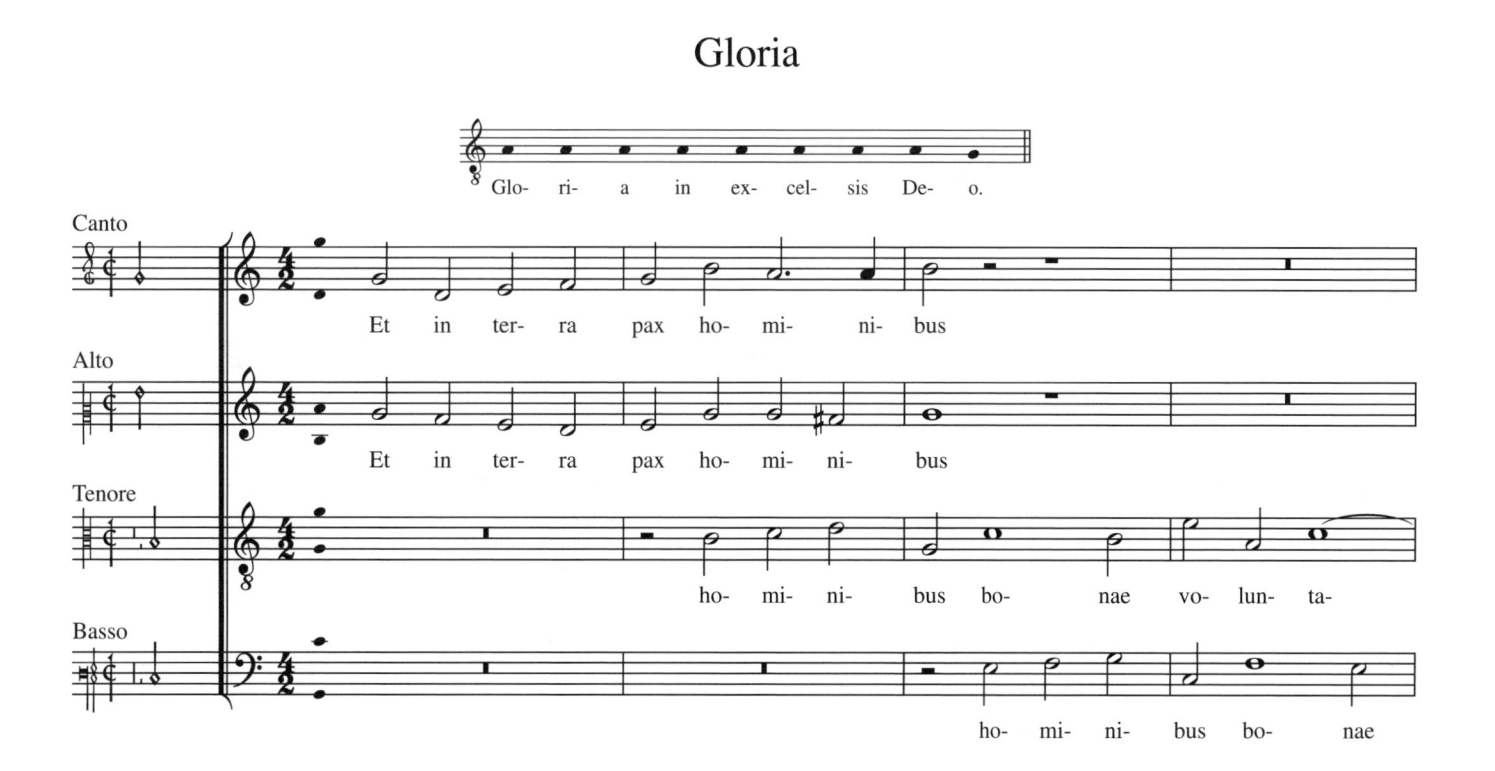

Gloria

Gloria in excelsis Deo.

5
Be- ne- di- ci- mus te.
Lau- da- mus te. Be- ne- di- ci- mus te. Ad-
- tis. Lau- da- mus te. Ad- - o- ra-
vo- lun- ta- tis. Be- ne- di- ci- mus te. Ad- - o- ra-
10
Glo- ri- - fi- ca- mus te. Gra- ti- as a- gi- mus
- o- ra- mus te. Glo- ri- fi- ca- mus te. Gra- ti- as a-
- mus te. Glo- ri- fi- ca- mus te. Gra- ti- as a-
- mus te. Gra- ti- as
15
ti- bi pro- pter ma- gnam glo- ri- am tu- am.
-gi- mus ti- bi pro- pter ma- gnam glo- ri- am tu- am. Do- mi- ne
-gi- mus ti- bi pro- - pter ma- gnam glo- ri- am tu- am. Do-
pro- pter ma- gnam glo- ri- am tu- am.

20
De- - us Pa- - ter om- ni- po-tens.
De- us, Rex cae- le- - stis, De- us Pa- ter om- ni- po-tens.
-mi- ne De- - us, Rex cae- le- stis, De- us Pa- ter om- ni- po-tens.
De- us Pa- ter om- ni- po-tens.
26
Do- mi- ne Fi- li Je- su Chri- ste.
u- ni- ge- ni- te Je- su Chri- ste.
u- ni- ge- ni- te Je- su Chri- ste. Do- mi- ne
Do- mi- ne Fi- li Je- su Chri- ste. Do- mi- ne
32
A- - gnus De- - i
A- gnus De- - i, Fi- li- us Pa-
De- us, Fi- li- us Pa-
De- us, A- gnus De- i, Fi- li- us Pa-

37
Qui tol- lis mi- - se- re- re no- bis. Qui
- tris. pec- ca- ta mun- - di Qui tol-
- tris. Qui tol- lis mi- se- re- re no- bis. Qui tol-
- tris. pec- ca- ta mun- - di Qui tol-
43
tol- lis pec- ca- ta mun- - di,
- - lis su- sci- pe, su- sci-
-lis pec- ca- ta mun- - - di, su- sci- pe,
- - lis pec- ca- ta mun- di, su- sci- pe,
48
de- pre- ca- ti- o- - nem no- stram.
-pe de- - pre- ca- ti- o- nem no- - stram. Qui se-
su- sci- pe de- pre- ca- ti- o- nem no- stram. Qui
su- sci- pe de- pre- ca- ti- o- nem no- stram. Qui

ad dextram Pa- / -des ad dextram Pa- / -se- -des mi- / se- -des ad dextram Patris, mise-

-tris, miserere nobis. / -tris Quoniam tu solus san- / -se- re- re no- bis. Quoniam tu solus san- / -re- re, miserere nobis. Quoniam tu solus san-

Tu solus Dominus. Je- su Chri- / -ctus. Tu solus Dominus. Je- su Christe, Jesu / -ctus. Tu solus Altissimus, Je- su Chri- / -ctus. Tu solus Altissimus, Je- su Chri-

69
- ste. Cum San- cto Spi- ri- tu, in glo- - ri- a
Chri- ste. Cum San- cto Spi- ri- tu, in glo- - ri- a
- ste. Cum San- cto Spi- ri- tu, De- i
- ste. Cum San- cto Spi- ri- tu, in glo- - ri- a De-
74
A- - men.
A- - - men.
Pa- tris. A- - men, a- -
- i Pa- tris. A- men, a- -
80
De- - i Pa- tris. A- - men.
De- - i Pa- tris. A- men, a- men.
- men. De- - i Pa- tris. A- men, a- men.
- men. De- - i Pa- tris. A- men, a- men.

Credo

16
Fi- li- um De- - i u- ni- ge- ni- tum.
Fi- li- um De- i u- ni- ge- ni- tum. Et ex
Fi- li- um De- i Et ex
Fi- li- um De- i u- ni- ge- ni- tum.
21
Pa- - tre na- tum an- te om- ni-
Pa- - tre na- tum an- te om- ni-
Et ex Pa- - tre na- tum an- te
26
De- um de De- o, De- um
-a sae- cu- la. lu- men de lu- mi- ne,
-a sae- cu- la. lu- men de lu- mi- ne,
om- ni- a sae- cu- la. De- um de De- o, De- um

31
ve- - rum Ge- ni- tum, non fa-
de De- o ve- ro. Ge- ni- tum, non fa- ctum,
de De- o ve- ro.
ve- - rum Ge- ni- tum, non fa-
36
-ctum, per quem om- ni- a
con- sub- stan- ti- a- lem Pa- tri: per quem om- ni- a
con- sub- stan- ti- a- lem Pa- tri: per quem om- ni- a
-ctum, per quem om- ni- a
41
fa- cta sunt. et pro- pter no- stram sa- lu- tem de-
fa- cta sunt. Qui pro- pter nos ho- - mi- nes,
fa- cta sunt. Qui pro- pter nos ho- - mi- nes,
fa- cta sunt. et pro- pter no- stram sa- lu- tem de-

47
-scen- - dit, de-
de- scen- - dit
et pro- pter no- stram sa- lu- tem de-
-scen- dit, de- scen- - - dit, de-
51
-scen- dit de cae- lis. Et in- car- na- tus est
Et in- car- na- - tus est de
-scen- dit de cae- lis. Et in- car- na- tus est de
-scen- dit de cae- lis. Et in- car- na- tus est de
56
ex Ma- ri- a Vir- gi-
Spi- ri- tu San- cto ex Ma- ri- a Vir- gi-
Spi- ri- tu San- cto
Spi- ri- tu San- cto ex Ma- ri- a Vir- gi-

61
-ne: et ho- mo fa- ctus est, et ho-
-ne: et ho- mo fa- ctus est, et ho-
et ho- mo
-ne: et ho- mo fa- ctus est, et ho-
67
-mo fa- ctus est. Cru- ci- fi- xus
-mo fa- ctus est. Cru- ci- fi- - xus
fa- - ctus est. e- ti- am pro
-mo fa- ctus est. e- ti-
73
sub Pon- ti- o Pi- la- to pas-
e- ti- am pro no- - bis: pas- -
no- - - bis
-am pro no- - bis: sub Pon- ti- o Pi- la- to

78
-sus, et se- pul- tus est. ter- ti- a di-
- sus, et se- pul- - tus est. Et re- sur- re- xit
Et re- sur- re- xit ter- ti- a
pas- sus, et se- pul- - tus est. Et re- sur- re- xit ter- ti- a
83
- e Et a- scen- dit in cae-
se- cun- dum Scri- ptu- - ras. Et a- scen-
di- e, se- cun- dum Scri- ptu- ras.
di- e Et a- scen- dit in
88
- lum Et i- te- rum
-dit in cae- lum: se- det ad de- xte- ram Pa- tris. Et i-
se- det ad de- xte- ram Pa- - tris. ven-
cae- lum: se- det ad de- xte- ram Pa- tris. ven-

93
ven- tu- rus est cum glo- ri- a, ju- di- ca- re vi-
- te- rum ju- di- ca- re vi- vos et
-tu- rus est cum glo- - ri- a, ju- di- ca- re vi-
-tu- rus est cum glo- ri- a, ju- di- ca- re vi- vos et
98
-vos et mor- tu- os: non e- rit, non e- rit
mor- tu- os: cu- jus re- gni non e- rit fi-
-vos et mor- tu- os: cu- jus re- gni non e- rit
mor- tu- os: non e- rit
103
fi- nis. Et in Spi- ri- tum San- ctum, Do- mi- num, et vi- vi- fi-
- nis. Et in Spi- ri- tum San- ctum, Do- mi- num, et vi- vi- fi-
fi- nis. Et in Spi- ri- tum San- ctum, Do- mi- num, et vi- vi- fi-
Et in Spi- ri- tum San- ctum, Do- mi- num, et vi- vi- fi-

108
- can- tem: qui ex Pa- tre Fi- li- o- que pro- ce- dit. Qui cum
-can- tem: qui ex Pa- tre Fi- li- o- que pro- ce- dit. Qui cum
-can- tem: qui ex Pa- tre Fi- li- o- que pro- ce- dit. Qui cum
-can- tem: qui ex Pa- tre Fi- li- o- que pro- ce- dit.
113
Pa- tre et Fi- li- o si- - mul ad- o- ra- tur, et con- glo- ri- fi-
Pa- tre et Fi- li- o si- mul ad- - o- ra- tur, et con- glo-
Pa- tre et Fi- li- o si- mul ad- o- ra- tur, et con- glo-
si- mul ad- o- ra- tur, et con- glo-
118
-ca- tur: qui lo- cu- tus est per Pro- phe- tas.
-ri- fi- ca- tur: per Pro- phe- tas.
-ri- fi- ca- tur: qui lo- cu- tus est per Pro- phe- tas. Et u-
-ri- fi- ca- tur: per Pro- phe- tas. Et u- nam

123
Et u- nam et a- po- sto- li- cam
Et u- nam san- ctam ca- tho- li- cam et a- po- sto- li-
-nam san- - ctam ca- tho- - li- cam
san- ctam ca- tho- li- cam et a- po- sto- li-
127
Ec- cle- si- am. in re- mis- si-
-cam Ec- cle- si- am. in
Con- fi- te- or u- num ba- pti- - sma
-cam Ec- cle- si- am. Con- fi- te- or u- num ba- pti- - sma
132
-o- nem pec- - ca- to- - - rum.
re- mis- si- o- nem pec- ca- to- rum.
pec- - ca- to- rum. Et ex- spe- cto re- sur-
Et ex- spe- cto re- sur-

137
Et vi-
mor- tu- o- - - rum.
-re- cti- o- nem mor- tu- o- - rum.
-re- cti- o- - nem mor- tu- o- rum. Et vi- tam ven-
142
-tam ven- tu- ri sae- cu- li. A- -
ven- tu- ri sae- cu- li. A- men,
Et vi- tam ven- tu- ri sae- cu- li. A- - men,
-tu- ri sae- cu- li. A- -
147
- men, a- - men, a- men, a- men, a- men.
a- - - men, a- men, a- men.
a- men, a- men, a- men.
- men, a- - - men, a- men, a- men, a- men.

Sanctus

16
- - ri- a tu- a.
glo- - ri- a tu- a. Ho- san- na in ex-
Ho- san- na in ex- cel-
-ri- a tu- a, glo- ri- a tu- a. Ho- san- na in ex- cel-
21
Ho- san- na in ex- cel- sis, in ex- cel- sis.
-cel- sis, ho- - san- na in ex- cel- sis, in ex- cel- sis.
- sis, ho- san- na in ex- cel- sis, in ex- cel- sis.
- sis, ho- san- na in ex- cel- sis, in ex- cel- sis.
27
Be- ne- di- ctus qui ve- - nit in no- mi- ne Do- mi-
Be- ne- di- ctus qui ve- nit
Be- ne- di- ctus qui ve- - nit in no- mi- ne Do- mi- ni,
Be- ne- di- ctus qui ve- - nit in no- mi- ne Do-

Agnus Dei

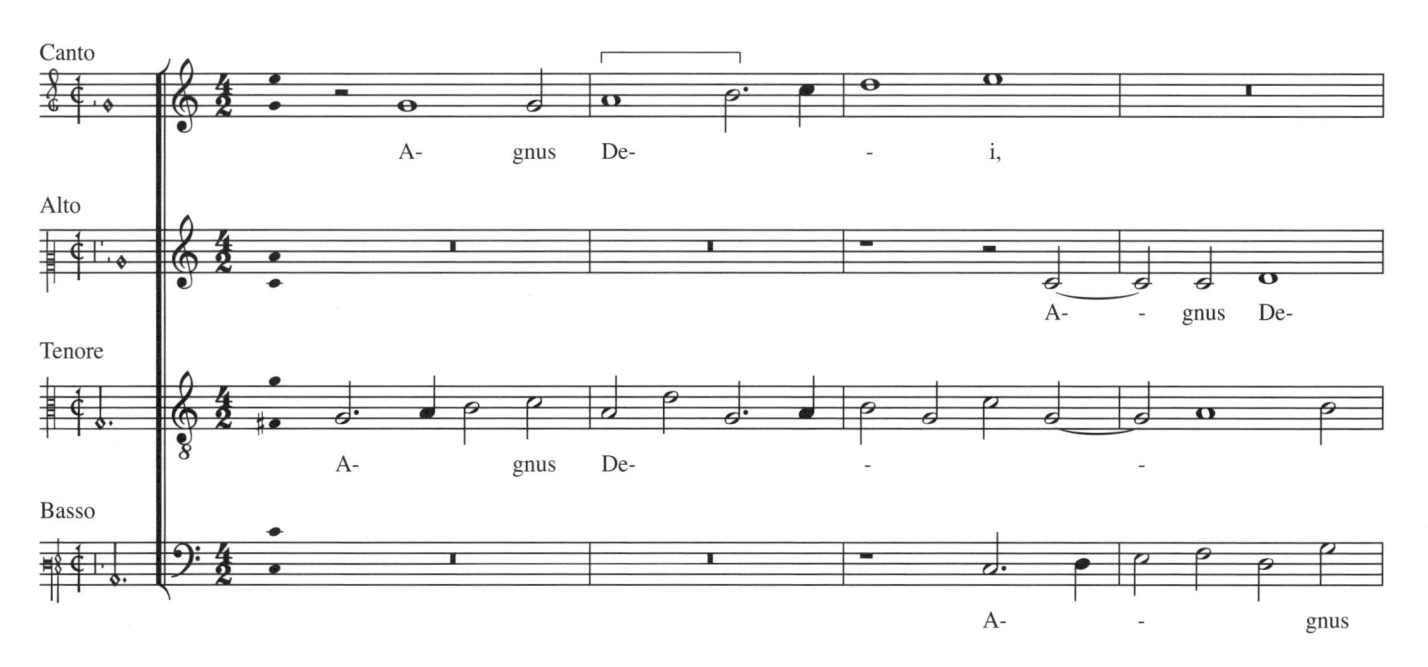

5
qui tol- lis pec- ca- - ta mun- - di, pec- ca- ta
- i, qui tol- lis pec- ca- ta mun- - di:
-i, qui tol- lis pec- ca- ta mun- - di,
De- i, qui tol- lis pec- ca- ta mun- - di, pec- ca- ta
11
mun- - di: mi- se-
mi- - se- re- re no- - bis,
pec- ca- ta mun- di: mi- se- re- re no- - bis,
mun- - di: mi- se- re- re no- - bis,
16
-re- re no- bis, mi- se- re- re no- - bis.
mi- se- re- re no- bis.
mi- se- re- re nobis, mi- se- re- - re no- - bis.
mi- se- re- re no- - bis.

Critical Report

Sources

Missae, Op. 13, 1677

The masses of opus 13 were principally edited from an original Sala print of Monferrato's 1677 publication, located in the Museo internazionale e biblioteca della musica di Bologna (I-Bc), RISM M3047. The title page of the publication reads:

> MISSAE | Ad usum Cappellarum | Quattuor, & Quinque Vocibus Concinendae. | NATALIS MONFERRATI | In Ducali Templo Santi MARCI Venetiarum | Magistri Musices. | OPUS DECIMUM TERTIUM. | DICATAE. | Illustrissimo, & Excellentissimo D. D. | VINCENTIO | AMULIO. | (device) | VENETIIS. | Apud Iosephum Salam. Anno 1677.

I-Bc's print, which is both complete and in excellent condition, comprises four partbooks labeled Canto, Alto, Tenor, Bassus (and Basso), and Organum.

Other sources of the print are located in the following archives: Brussels, Bibliothèque royale de Belgique (B-Br), incomplete source, partbooks (C, A, T, B); Wiesentheid, Musiksammlung des Grafen von Schönborn-Wiesentheid (D-WD), complete source, partbooks (C, A, T, B, Org.); Paris, Conservatoire national de musique (F-Pc), incomplete source, partbooks (C, A, T, B); Paris, Bibliothèque nationale de France (F-Pn), complete source, partbooks (C, A, T, B, Org.); Bologna, Basilica di San Petronio (I-Bsp), incomplete source, partbooks (C, A, T, B); Pistoia, Cattedrale di San Zeno (I-PS), complete source, partbooks (C, A, T, B, Org.). The legibility of the print in I-Bc is not surpassed in any of the other sources.

The fourth and sixth masses from opus 13 also survive in late-seventeenth-century choirbooks in San Marco's archive of pre-nineteenth-century music.[1] These sources of the masses are distinguished hereafter by the prefix LC (*libro da coro*). Thus, "LC/op.13/IV," discussed below, signifies a reading of the fourth mass from opus 13, which exists in a choirbook at San Marco.

The source LC/op.13/IV is bound together with (and follows) a copy of the first mass from opus 19, LC/op.19/I. Both masses were copied by the priest Lorenzo Rossi, and they are dated similarly 1677. The large choirbook measures 74 × 49 cm (see plates 8–11). In typical fashion, all of the voices of the composition are written separately: the upper voice is on the top left-hand page, the lowest is at the bottom of the right-hand page. The choirbook source LC/op.13/VI containing the sixth mass of opus 13—the only mass included in this choirbook—is dated 1678 (one year after the same mass was published in opus 13); the copyist is unknown.[2] This choirbook measures 76 × 48.5 cm (see plates 12–13). Unlike the published opus 13 print, these choirbooks contain no continuo part, a trait consistent with other a cappella material in the early Marciana archive.

The title page of LC/op.13/IV reads:

> MISSA | QUATUOR VOCIBUS | AUCTORE | R. D. NATALE MONFERRATO | IN ECCLESIA DIVI MARCI | MAGISTRO. | ANNO 1677. | LAURENTIUS DE RUBEIS VENETUS SCRIBEBAT.

The title page of LC/op.13/VI reads:

> Missa Quinque Vocibus | D. Natalis Monferrati | In Ecclesia Ducali S. Marci | Magistri Musices.

Nineteenth-century transcriptions of the two opus 13 masses in San Marco's *libri da coro* are preserved in Venice's Biblioteca Nazionale Marciana (I-Vnm). The transcriptions, arranged in score, originate from the early music collection of Lorenzo Canal, a late-nineteenth-century canon of San Marco.[3] They include two copies transcribed from LC/op.13/IV and one taken from LC/op.13/VI.[4]

While all of the masses from opus 13 were edited predominantly from Sala's print (as mentioned), the existence of the choirbook sources could not be ignored. It is to be expected that Monferrato, as the composer, and working in close partnership with Sala, was fully acquainted with the musical text of opus 13. Equally, the choirbook sources of the opus 13 masses must also have been familiar to him; indeed, maestro Monferrato likely directed the choir from the music presented on their folios. It would be fruitless to attempt a pecking order for this source material, since the readings are predominantly concordant. The few variants in the choirbooks have been incorporated in this edition where Sala's print is unclear, where its reading is questionable, or where its musical and textual solutions are considered inferior to those offered by the choirbooks. These matters are detailed fully in the critical notes. By contrast, while the secondary sources in I-Vnm provide useful evidence of musical and social trends in nineteenth-century Venice, they were rejected here in view of the availability of excellent primary source material.

Messe et Magnificat, Op. 19, 1682

The masses of opus 19 were edited predominantly from an original Sala print of Monferrato's 1682 (1681 *more veneto*) publication located in Paris's Bibliothèque nationale de France (F-Pn), RISM M3051. This is the sole surviving source for the print. The title page reads:

> MESSE | ET MAGNIFICAT | A QUATTRO VOCI | Composti Per uso di Capelle. | DI D. NATALE MONFERRATO | Maestro di Capella Nella Ducal in Venetia. | DEDICATI | All'Illustrissimo, & Eccellentissimo Signor Procurator | GIO: MOROSINI | OPERA XVIIII. | (device) | IN VENETIA, M.DC.LXXXI. | APPRESSO Giuseppe Sala.

F-Pn's print, which is both complete and in excellent condition, comprises four partbooks labeled Canto, Alto, Tenore, and Basso; no continuo part is included.

As mentioned above, the opening mass from opus 19 survives in a late-seventeenth-century choirbook in San Marco's archive of pre-nineteenth-century music.[5] This source, LC/op.19/I, is bound together with (and precedes) LC/op.13/IV. The title page of LC/op.19/I reads:

> MISSA | Quatuor Vocibus, | Auctore | A. R. D. Natale Monferrato | In Ecclesia Ducali Divi | Marci Magistro. | Anno 1677. | Laurentius de Rubeis Venetus | Scribebat.

Nineteenth-century transcriptions of LC/op.19/I are preserved in Venice's Biblioteca Nazionale Marciana (I-Vnm) and Procuratoria di San Marco (I-Vsm). The transcription in I-Vnm, arranged in score, originates from the early music collection of Lorenzo Canal.[6] The transcription in I-Vsm contains a score and a set of fifteen vocal parts (two soprano, four alto, four tenor, and five bass), all of which originate from the LC.[7]

For the reasons given in relation to those masses in opus 13 that also survive in early choirbooks, minor variants offered by LC/op.19/I have been interpolated in the critical text of this edition. The nineteenth-century source material for this mass has been rejected in view of the availability of excellent primary source material.

Editorial Methods

Titles, Labels, and Text Underlay

The editorial titles of the opus 13 masses, which are given in Italian, specify the type of composition as *messa a cappella*. In the opus 13 print, which contains multiple settings for four voices, the masses are numbered in Italian as "Messa prima," "Messa seconda," and so forth, and this system has been incorporated in the editorial titles of opus 13. In contrast, the two masses of opus 19 are not numbered in the edition, since they can be distinguished as *Messa a cappella* for the first and *Messa breve* for the second. This differs from the original titles of the masses in the opus 19 print, which are "Missa prima" and "Missa brevis secunda," respectively. As to the movements of the masses, their standard Latin headings are added editorially.

With regard to the text underlay, the sources use the Latin form of the Ordinary given in the *Missale Romanum* (leaving aside minor orthographic variants). For consistency, the Latin underlay for the masses has been tacitly revised with regard to capitalization and spelling, and punctuation has been added, all in accordance with the versions of the Ordinary texts given in the *Liber Usualis*.

In typical fashion, the sources incorporate two forms of textual abbreviation. In the first case, the word "et" is commonly substituted by the ampersand (&); in the second, repetition of a textual fragment is frequently denoted by either the symbol *ii* or *ij*. In this edition, all ampersands have been tacitly revised as "Et/et." Since not all abbreviations represented by *ii* or *ij* can be expanded without ambiguity, their corresponding editorial expansions are enclosed in angle brackets (< >).

In the Kyrie movements of both opuses 13 and 19, it is generally unclear whether the word "eleison" should be divided as "e-lei-son" or "e-le-i-son." In this edition, the latter division has been favored in passages that are textually ambiguous.

Finally, the intonations "Gloria in excelsis Deo" and "Credo in unum Deum," which should precede the Gloria and Credo movements, respectively (and are usually sung by the celebrant), do not appear in the prints. In this edition, Gregorian chants have been quoted from the *Liber Usualis* and are suggested at the appropriate points in the masses. Due to the scant availability of chants assigned to the text of the Credo, there has been some repetition and tonal reworking of intoning material for this movement in this edition. In the Credos of the *Messa a cappella seconda* and the *Messa a cappella sesta* (both from opus 13), the opening chant has been transposed for tonal suitability.

Format

The vocal parts of the sources have been retained, except in the *Messa a cappella quarta*, where, due to the wide-ranging tessitura of the Alto part—commonplace in all-male choirs, especially those incorporating *castrati*—the alto part has been revised as Tenore 1. Vocal parts are ordered from highest to lowest, with the basso continuo part of opus 13 appearing underneath. In the masses of opus 19, which were published without a basso continuo part, no editorial continuo part has been added since this would not only be unnecessary—the continuo harmony is readily evident from the vocal parts—but also would compromise the principle of editorial restraint practiced elsewhere.

Initial source clefs are shown in the incipits of each composition. The various clef changes occurring subsequently within movements of the sources are only reported in those circumstances where incorrect clef usage occurs in the source. In this edition, modern clefs have been assigned in accordance with tessitura. The basso continuo part (which, by way of its *basso seguente* formation, tracks notation in both high and low registers) uses the treble (G2) clef for phrases that reach above the level of f'; the bass (F4) clef is used elsewhere. The clef changes in the edition are not necessarily at the same points or clefs as the clef changes found in the source; as these differences are matters only of appearance, the adjustments have been made tacitly. Key and meter signatures have been retained with the exception of the *alla breve* signature. Since the latter signifies $\frac{4}{2}$, as opposed to $\frac{2}{2}$ in modern notation, it has been replaced by a $\frac{4}{2}$ signature. Redundant meter signatures have been removed without comment. Proportional relationships have been suggested with equations at points of juncture where triple-time and duple-time measures meet. The equations are placed above the relevant measures of the system.

As the prints originate from a time that precedes the convention for regular measure lengths, editorial barlines have been tacitly provided; any original barlines not distinguished in the edition are reported in the critical notes. Final barlines in all masses are editorial, replacing double barlines. All other double barlines that demarcate sections have been retained; the addition or removal of double barlines is reported in the critical notes.

Notation

Both the pitch and duration of the original notation have been preserved in this edition, as indicated in the incipits of each composition. Due to the application of editorial barlines, it has been necessary to update particular notational conventions of the sources: specifically, where longas in the prints exceed the duration of an editorial measure, these have been replaced with equivalent modern notation—dotted breve, breve, or semibreve, as determined by the measure—with fermata; where a breve occurs in triple time without augmentation dot, the latter has been added to fill out the editorial measure; where a breve and semibreve are tied, they have been replaced by a single equivalent note (as dotted breve); and, finally, where a note exceeds the duration of an editorial bar, it has been replaced with an equivalent combination of tied notes. Since, in these circumstances, it is only the presentation of the notation that has changed, all such amendments have been made tacitly. Where fermatas have been added to notes or rests that are not longas, the fermatas as well as the notes or rests are reported.

Other editorial modifications to the notation have also been made in relation to the following. Single notes that are stemmed upward on the middle staff line have been stemmed downward. All beaming is editorial. Notes and rests lacking in the sources have been added in brackets in the edition. *Note nere*, which draw attention to syncopations in triple-time passages, are reproduced as conventional notes and are marked by open horizontal brackets. Similarly, two-note ligatures (indicating that two semibreves should be sung to one syllable of text) are marked by closed horizontal brackets. Both types of brackets are placed above vocal staves and below basso continuo staves. Slurs are used inconsistently in vocal parts; these have consequently been removed and are reported in the critical notes.

The prints employ a system of chromatic alteration that operated before the advent of regular barring, namely, an accidental (as a rule) applies only to the note it immediately precedes or to closely repeated notes of the same pitch, even if a rest intervenes. In this edition, this system has been updated so that an accidental remains in force throughout a measure unless canceled.

Editorial accidentals are placed in square brackets. Source accidentals that have become redundant because of editorial barlines have been tacitly removed. Since the sources do not use naturals (flats and sharps are used to cancel sharps and flats, respectively), natural symbols have been substituted as required without comment. Editorial cautionary accidentals (placed in parentheses on the staff) have been added sparingly to provide clarification where tonalities are either truly ambiguous or unexpectedly transitional.

Basso continuo Figures

Monferrato's music is figured sparsely in the seventeenth-century manner. The existing figures have been retained with a minimum of additions, since the score format reduces the necessity for figures. Modifications have been made only where the original figures are incorrect or where an editorially modified harmony requires a revision to the figures. Editorial suggestions have been offered in the few places where an appropriate realization is not readily evident. Three types of modification have been made without comment: first, misaligned figures—commonplace in seicento sources—have been placed in their correct metrical positions; second, accidentals are uniformly placed before (not after) the numeral to which they refer; and third, where stacked figures place the smaller number above the larger number (as $\frac{3}{5}$), the modern convention is applied without comment (as $\frac{5}{3}$). Figures added editorially appear in brackets; all other revisions or emendations to original figures are reported in the critical notes.

Performance Directions

The vast majority of performance directions in the sources are to be found in the basso continuo part of opus 13. These are intended as cues, either to indicate what or how many voices are singing at a given point, or to indicate the text that is being sung. Directions that mention scoring (e.g., "A3") are positioned to the left of the staff in the source; those that relate to the text are placed below it. Since opus 19 omits the basso continuo part entirely, cues are accordingly infrequent; they are located to the left of the staff, and they refer only to the text. Since the masses are presented in score in this edition, all voicing and text cues have been tacitly removed.

Critical Notes

These notes report specific aspects of the sources that are not retained in this edition. The notes are arranged in order of location (by measure number), vocal or instrumental part, then the reading. The following abbreviations are used: C = Canto, A = Alto, T = Tenore, Q = Quinto, B = Basso, and B.c. = Basso continuo; additionally, I-Vsm signifies a reading from the choirbook sources in Venice, Procuratoria di San Marco, for the fourth mass of opus 13 (LC/op.13/IV, Cat. no. 1930/ii), the sixth mass of opus 13 (LC/op.13/VI, Cat. no. 1929), and the first mass of opus 19 (LC/op.19/I, Cat. no. 1930/i). Pitches are specified by the system whereby c' represents middle C.

Messa a cappella prima

Kyrie

M. 27, B.c., note 1 is followed by single barline. M. 51, B.c., note 1 figured "4 3."

Gloria

M. 27, B.c., + sign written beneath note 1. M. 27, B.c., note 2 figured "4 3." M. 48, B.c., note 1 figured "7." M. 103, B.c., note 5 (semibreve—tied to m. 104 in edition) figured "2 3."

Credo

M. 30, B.c., + sign written beneath note 1. M. 30, B.c., note 2 figured "6." M. 55, C, note 3 is minim. M. 77, C, A, T, B.c., measure concludes with double barline. M. 77, C, A, breve rest and breve, respectively, lacks fermata; fermatas added in edition per T, B, and B.c. parts. M. 126, B.c., note 1 figured "4." M. 144, B.c., + sign written beneath note 2. M. 154, B.c., < sign written beneath note 1 (placed on the second line of the staff), perhaps to warn of lacuna in measures 156–65. Mm. 156–65, B.c., notation is lacking for these measures, so it has been added by the editor. M. 167, A, note is e'.

Sanctus

M. 1, B.c., note 1 figured "2 3." M. 3, B.c., note 4 (semibreve—tied to m. 4 in edition) figured "2 3." M. 70, C, note is d".

Messa a cappella seconda

The positioning of textual syllables is unclear in the source in many places. This matter has been addressed without comment.

Kyrie

M. 3, B.c., note 5 (semibreve—tied to m. 4 in edition) figured "4 3." M. 50, B.c., note 1 figured "5 6."

Gloria

M. 2, A, horizontal line drawn through stem of note 1. M. 36, B.c., + sign written beneath note 1. M. 47, B.c., + sign written beneath note 1. M. 110, A, note 3 (ligated semibreve—tied to m. 111 in edition) is d'.

Credo

M. 108, B.c., measure concludes with single barline. M. 138, A, note 2 is semiminim. Mm. 154–61, A, incorrect C4 clef used. M. 155, A, horizontal line drawn through stem of note 2.

Agnus Dei

M. 8, B.c., measure concludes with single barline.

Messa a cappella terza

Kyrie

M. 13, B, note is minim. Mm. 26–30, A, incorrect C4 clef used. Mm. 37–43, A, incorrect C4 clef used. M. 41, B.c., figures "4" and "3" written above notes 2 and 3, respectively.

Gloria

M. 20, B.c., + sign written beneath note 1. M. 42, B.c., note 1 figured "7 2."

Credo

M. 70, A, notes 1–2 are g'–d'. M. 81, B.c., figure "4" written above note 3; moved to m. 82, note 1 in edition. M. 123, B.c., + sign written beneath note 1. M. 144, B.c., note 2 figured "6 5."

Messa a cappella quarta

Kyrie

M. 1, B.c., note 3 (dotted semibreve—tied to m. 2 in edition) figured "5 6." M. 8, B.c., note 3 (dotted semibreve—tied to m. 9 in edition) figured "5 6."

Gloria

M. 72, B, + sign written beneath note 3. M. 91, B.c., note 4 (semibreve—tied to m. 92 in edition) figured "5 6." M. 93, B.c., note 1 has ♭.

Credo

M. 146, B.c., note 1 figured "6 5." M. 149, B.c., figure "3" placed above note 2. M. 166, C, note 3, ♯ given in I-Vsm.

Sanctus

Mm. 35–62, T1, the music in these measures is sung instead by the T2 part in I-Vsm; the T1 measures of I-Vsm are marked "tacet."

Agnus Dei

M. 16, B, note 2, ♭ given in I-Vsm.

Messa a cappella quinta

Credo

M. 134, A, note 1 is minim.

Agnus Dei

Mm. 4–12, A, incorrect C3 clef used from beat 3 of m. 4 to beat 2 of m. 12. M. 22, B.c., note 3 figured "5 ♯5."

Messa a cappella sesta

Kyrie

M. 66, A, whole rest given in I-Vsm.

Gloria

M. 1, B.c., note 1 figured "2." M. 34, B.c., + sign written beneath note 1. M. 67, A, note 2 is e', f' given in I-Vsm. M. 68, Q, note 2 is a, b♭ given in I-Vsm. M. 81, B.c., + sign written beneath note 1.

CREDO

M. 50, B.c., note 4 figured "4 3."   M. 74, A, note 2 is e', c' given in I-Vsm.   M. 74, B.c., note 2 figured "6 5."   M. 149, B.c., note 1 figured "4 3."

SANCTUS

M. 3, C, note 2 is b♭', g' given in I-Vsm.   M. 59, B.c., note 1 figured "6 ♯7."

Messa a cappella

KYRIE

Mm. 29–30, B, text of m. 29, notes 2–4 and m. 30, note 1 given in I-Vsm.

GLORIA

Mm. 96–97, T2, slur from note 4 of m. 96 to note of m. 97.   M. 97, C, measure concludes with single barline.

CREDO

Mm. 43–44, A, slur from note 2 of m. 43 to note 2 of m. 44.   Mm. 44–45, T2, slur from note 3 of m. 44 to note of m. 45.   Mm. 71–74, B, rests include five breve rests rather than the necessary four.   M. 78, A, notes 2–3 slurred.   M. 135, T2, note 2, ♯ given in I-Vsm.   M. 180, A, rest given in I-Vsm.   M. 187, A, ♯ given in I-Vsm.

SANCTUS

M. 20, A, note 2 is followed by single barline.   M. 41, B.c., note 6 has ♭.

Messa breve

GLORIA

M. 12, B, measure concludes with single barline.

CREDO

M. 18, C, note 2 is b'.   M. 69, T, note is e'.   M. 79, C, note 1 is b'.

Notes

1. I-Vsm, Cat. nos. 1930/ii and 1929, respectively. This form of reference comes from Francesco Passadore and Franco Rossi, *San Marco: Vitalità di una tradizione*, 4 vols. (Venice: Edizioni Fondazione Levi, 1994), 4:1484–86.

2. Passadore and Rossi have hypothesized that the copyist was Lorenzo Rossi. See Passadore and Rossi, *San Marco*, 1:71–73.

3. For a brief history of nineteenth-century transcriptions of early music at San Marco, see Jonathan R. J. Drennan, "Giovanni Rovetta's 'Missa brevis': A Symbol of Musical Longevity," *Recercare* 22 (2010): 125–44.

4. Canal's copies are shelfmarked Cod. It. IV-1325 (=11135).

5. I-Vsm, Cat. no. 1930/i.

6. I-Vnm, Cod. It. IV-1325 (=11135).

7. The score in I-Vsm has the call number B.812; the parts, B.812/1–15.